Balancing Organisational and Personal Development Needs

Balancing Organisational and Personal Development Needs

By

Sue Lillyman and Carol Ward

Quay Books
Mark Allen Publishing Ltd

Quay Books, Division of Mark Allen Publishing Limited, Jesses Farm, Snow Hill, Dinton, Nr Salisbury, Wilts, SP3 5HN

ISBN 1 85642 100 7

British Library Cataloguing-in-Publication Data
A catalogue record for this book is available from the British Library

Printed in the UK by The Cromwell Press, Trowbridge, Wiltshire

Contents

Acknowledgements

Primarily we would like to thank the participants involved in career profiling and the organisations who provided the opportunity to develop other approaches such as strategies, systems and standards, as described in the book.

Individually we would like to thank Maggie Atherton, Tessa Clarke, David Cox, Sonia Lloyd, Dianne Whitfield and our families for their continuous support.

Foreword

This publication is timely, with less and less people available to do more and more complicated healthcare delivery, it is so important to ensure quality of care through managing performance and career profiling. Pressures on organisations, and the people working in them, are common features of the late 20th century. These pressures are given euphemisms such as 'challenges' and 'developments'. We use words such as 'interesting' when we really mean 'worrying' or 'fearful'. Life at work for some people is not a happy experience. They worry about doing the 'right thing' in the right way, and are sometimes at a loss to know how to find out new information and new techniques. Therefore, anything that can be done to support people at work and to make the fit between the individual and the organisation more meaningful and relevant will be an advantage.

The links between the individual and the organisation are crucial in promoting and sustaining a quality business. The majority of people who work in the public sector, and particular in the health sector, want to do the very best they can for the community or communities they serve.

In this book we are presented with a review of the literature around individuals and organisational learning, with a strong focus on experiential learning. Learning through experience can happen serendipitously, but it often needs as much as energy and focus as more traditional forms of education. It is important to identify for people that learning is a lifelong activity, that brings theory and practice together, that it may apply to the workplace in this context, but actually affects or influences many other aspects of a person's life. The current emphasis on clinical governance and clinical effectiveness are underpinned by the demand for keeping current knowledge of issues alive and refreshed. And clinical activity is not just about clinical practice, it is about management of clinical practice, education for practice and researching into practice. So there can be no one in the NHS who does not need to have their learning needs identified, and where possible linked into a personal career profile, for their own benefit of course, but also for the organisation's benefit and more importantly patient's and client's benefit.

This book provides a template for starting a performance management system, or if there is a system already in place, of revisiting it, and refreshing it if necessary. This is a need which will not go away, which has to be addressed, and the time to do it is now.

Margaret Bamford

Introduction

This book provides a two tier, macro and micro, view of approaches to career development. It will review career planning and development from both the individual and the organisations' perspectives.

As the individual nurse, midwife and health visitor has become responsible and accountable for their competence in their clinical practice they will need to plan their future development. This development can no longer be left to an ad hoc arrangement and therefore a process of career development will need to be addressed. The individual will have to develop their needs to meet governmental, organisational and professional requirements.

As the opportunities and requirements for individual development expand, and become more complex, a framework to support these individuals will need to be developed. This book examines several of the frameworks and strategies available for both the organisation and individual practitioner. These frameworks will address the professional governmental constraints in which the individual plans their career.

In addition the last chapter considers an alternative model, that of career profiling which can truly bridge the potential gap between individual and organisational development needs.

1

Developing the professional practitioner

Career development according to Cormack (1990), is the means by which the individual practitioner's contributions to healthcare are maximised. For this to occur it is imperative that each individual continually maintains and develops their knowledge base and clinical competence. This has been further echoed by the United Kingdom Central Council (UKCC) in their documents Post Registration Education and Practice (UKCC, 1990) requirements and the Code of Professional Conduct (UKCC, 1992). These documents note the importance of clinical development and the responsibility for the individual practitioner to identify their development throughout their chosen career. This chapter will then attempt to identify how these issues have arisen within nursing and midwifery practice.

History of nursing

Florence Nightingale initially defined a good nurse as a 'good woman'. Nursing was seen in society as a caring occupation for those individuals who were of good character, from an appropriate social background and had high standards (Jones, 1994). The discipline of nursing has slowly evolved from this role of women, through apprenticeship, humanitarian aims, religious ideals, intuition, common sense, trial and error, theories and research (Shaw, 1993).

As nursing practice has evolved so has formal training for the nurse and midwife. Denny (1997) highlighted that it was through the British Nursing Association (BNA) that entrance was gained for the first nurse training at Guys, The Westminster, The London and Royal Free Hospitals in the late 1800's. The training involved the acquisition of scientific knowledge which was primarily from outside the practice setting and this was particularly from medicine. Training programmes for nurses and midwives at this stage were viewed as an apprenticeship, where much of the students' time was spent in the clinical environment. This continued through to the 1970's where Stein (1978) confirmed the subordinate role of the nurse in relation to the medical staff. However at this stage he noted the influence that the nurses held over the doctors in that decisions were made, and suggested, by the nurse in such a way that the medical staff took the credit. The doctor continued to maintain patriarchal control over the nurse to whom he delegated aspects of patient care and role of the 'handmaiden' was much in evidence.

Doctors continued to keep control of diagnosis and treatment. They welcomed the assistance of nurses in the task of monitoring and carrying out prescribed interventions. However as nursing developed, so a hierarchical structure had emerged within the nursing profession. The matron now had control of nursing staff. Individual accountability although identified through the training, was not particularly evident. Often the accountability was passed to a higher member of staff. It was the Salmon Report (DHSS, 1966) that introduced a managerial model into nursing and the power of the matron was finally broken. This report provided a way for the National Health Service to value clinical nurses and nurse specialists as they were now having closer contact with patients.

A further reorganisation of the NHS followed the Griffiths Report (DHSS, 1983). This provided the role of general management into the NHS and an emphasis on quality care was evident. At this stage nurses, midwives and health visitors were required to articulate the value of professional practice. The increasing drive for professionalisation and academic recognition within nursing itself (UKCC, 1986; ENB, 1991; UKCC, 1994) further promoted a substantial change in the delivery of care and the striving for further development for the individual practitioner. The focus was now directly on practice (Conway, 1996).

At the beginning of the 1990's, nurse training moved into mainstream higher education. The registration of qualified practitioners moved to that of diplomate level. Practitioners began to distinguish, in their practice, between what was termed 'basic nursing care' and the theory of practice. This theory related to medical knowledge and information about disease and nursing care to the practical process of nursing. The striving for professional status became evident.

Traditionally nurse training had occurred in schools of nursing, that were situated within the hospital complex. This changed as the schools and colleges merged and became part of higher educational institutions. It was during this period Jones (1994) notes that, with the introduction of academic study and the demise of the apprenticeship system the concept of the independent practitioner emerged.

Accountability now became a major concern for all practitioners. The Code of Professional Conduct (UKCC, 1984) introduced the extended role, this later changed to the expanded role (UKCC, 1992) and emphasis was placed on the individual as an accountable practitioner. Other influencing factors were introduced with the introduction of *The Patient's Charter* (DoH, 1991), standards of practice were identified and clients/patients became aware of their rights. There was also an increase in the expectation from the general public in relation to the quality of the service provision.

Nurse education provided a balance of knowledge, attitudinal change and skill, and included substantial breadth and depth of material.

Traditionally, training had focused on what nurses 'should do', rather than on 'why'. It had emphasised a reactive rather than proactive approach.

As healthcare professionals have developed and acquired a specialist body of nursing and midwifery competence in practice, the maintaining and development of that competence is paramount for the continued development and quality of a service provision (UKCC, 1990).

Academic, clinical and professional development

Professional development/competence can be divided into three aspects: academic, clinical and professional.

Academic development

Career development for those who wish to pursue the academic and hierarchical ladder is not a pre requisition for maintaining registration on a given part of the United Kingdom Central Council (UKCC) Register. It is by choice that the individual progresses up the academic levels. However the goal of continuing education is to enhance the practitioner's growth and improve nursing care, the latter being the most critical for quality assurance (Koyama *et al,* 1996). As nurses, midwives and health visitors are introduced to the academic arena of diploma, degree, masters and doctorate level of study many nurses will welcome the opportunity to chose a career pathway that provides opportunity for further study. As Bowles and Cassidy (1997) have identified, there is an emergence of the nurse practitioner, specialist practitioner and advanced practitioner. It is increasingly apparent that in order to gain the specialist status, the individual will not only have to gain the relevant experience in their chosen field of practice, but also be a graduate, as identified in the English National Board *Creating the Life Long Learner* (ENB, 1994) documents. The continuing debate for specialist and advanced practice and its relationship to higher academic status is currently under review by the UKCC. At present these posts are identified locally within the Trust and new roles developed that reflect the local needs. Academic development, as stated, is usually optional for individuals who wish to gain higher status, and not necessarily a goal for all practitioners.

Clinical development

It is this aspect of development that is mandatory for all practitioners, as stated in the UKCC's Post Registration Education and Practice (PREP) requirements (UKCC, 1990). For individual practitioners, clinical development is not just for those practitioners who wish to progress up the hierarchical and academic ladders. Clinical development is a requirement for all those individual practitioners within the healthcare arena who wish to remain on the UKCC register (UKCC, 1990).

Each practitioner will be required to demonstrate how

they have maintained and developed their clinical competence in their practice on a continual basis. This clinical development relates dirctly to the care that is being given by a practitioner to a client or client group. It involves the practitioners underpinning knowledge that supports their care and the research that informs the practice. The authors argue that this clinical development can be addressed and identified through the process of career development.

With the introduction of mandatory updating and development the notion of career development has become an issue not only for practitioners but also one which must be addressed by employers and healthcare providers.

Professional development

Professional development, like clinical, is also mandatory as it is identified in the same UKCC documents. This aspect of development relates to the ethical issues, law and quality of care being delivered to the client. The healthcare arena is in a state of continual change and together with the publication of the New NHS white paper (DoH, 1997) the profession must look at how the individual and employer will respond together in order to meet the continuing demand for quality care. Redfern and Norman (1990) argued that high quality of nursing care is the right of all patients, and it is the responsibility of each practitioner who delivers that care to ensure that this is provided.

In order for the practitioner to keep pace with these changes in practice, Lee (1991) argues that learning must continue throughout the individuals professional career, and that the nursing profession must develop independent practitioners capable of responding to that rapid change. These individuals must be aware of the legal and ethical aspects of their care as well as the clinical aspects of the delivering of that care.

The UKCC (1995) support the notion of continual development stating that:

> *Nurses, Midwives and Health Visitors practice in an environment of constant change, with new expanding roles for health professionals, increasing technological*

> *advances in treatment and care, and continuing reorganisation of resources. It is vital that you continue to develop your knowledge and competence throughout your career in order to cope with these demands and complexities of professional practice.'*

In an age of litigation, patient's rights, the purchaser/provider model and internal market forces, the practitioner must be conscious of their continual development of practice and be ready to be held accountable for the care they deliver.

Macro and micro approaches to career development

Nursing, midwifery and health visiting must produce and develop the areas of clinical and professional care as noted above.

The organisation, manager and employer's responsibility to staff development and the individual's responsibility in meeting and identifying their own developmental needs are addressed in following chapters. They are identified as the macro (organisational) and micro (individual) perspectives of career development. Both perspectives will review the current government and professional forces that must be met by both parties in order to develop a competent workforce. It will attempt to identify how the two, the organisational and individual, can come together to identify a pathway for practitioners to demonstrate their development and provision of competent professional conduct within clinical practice. *Chapter 7* provides an additional framework for the manager and individual to work together to identify this developmental process.

The Macro aspects will concentrate on the organisational issues and demonstrate frameworks which the organisation and the individual manager can utilise to meet the both areas developmental needs. The micro aspects will then review the same issues from the individual practitioner's perspective, discussing how the individual can incorporate these demands into the growing constraints on their time.

Systems that are currently employed will be reviewed from both perspectives, with an alternate approach discussed in *Chapter 7*, this is career profiling which builds on concepts of continual professional development and a personal development profile. We believe career profiling is a system which can truly bridge the potential gaps in identifying individual and organisations development needs.

References

Bowles N, Cassidy A (1997) Developing practitioners *Nursing Management* **4**(3): 8–9

Conway J (1996) *Nursing Expertise and Advanced Practice.* Quay Books, Mark Allen Publishing, Dinton

Cormack D (1990) *Developing Your Career in Nursing. Chapman Hall, London*

Denny E (1997) The second missing link: bible nursing in 19th century. *J Adv Nurs* **26**:1175–82

Department of Health (1991) *The Patient's Charter.* HMSO, London

Department of Health (1997) *The New NHS: Modern and Dependable.* HMSO, London

Department of Health and Social Services (1966) *Salmon Report* HMSO, London

Department of Health and Social Services (1983) *NHS Management Enquiry (Griffiths Report).* DHSS, London

English National Board (1991) *Framework for Continuing Professional Education for Nurses, Midwives and Health Visitors Guide to Implementation.* ENB, London

English National Board (1994) *Creating Life Long Learners.* ENB, London

Jones L (1994) *The Social Context of Health and Health Work.* Macmillan, London

Koyama M, Holzemer W, Kaharu C, *et al* (1996) Assessment of a continuing education evaluation framework. *J Cont Educa Nurs* **27**(3): 115–19

Lee T (1991) Students and contracts. *Senior Nurs* **11**(1): 33–5

Redfern S, Norman I (1990) Measuring the quality of nursing care: a consideration of different approaches. *J Adv Nurs* **15:**1260-1271

Shaw M (1993) The discipline of nursing: historical roots, current perspectives, future directions *J Adv Nurs* 18: 1651–6

Stein L (1978) *Reading in Sociology of Nursing Edinburgh.* Churchill Livingstone, Edinburugh

United Kingdom Central Council (1984) *Code of Professional Conduct for the Nurse, Midwife and Health Visitor 2nd ed.* UKCC, London

United Kingdom Central Council (1986) *Project 2000: A New Preparation for Practice.* UKCC, London

United Kingdom Central Council (1990) *Post Registration Education and Practice Project.* UKCC, London

United Kingdom Central Council (1992) *Code of Professional Conduct.* UKCC, London

United Kingdom Central Council (1994) *Post Registration Education and Practice Recommendations.* UKCC, London

United Kingdom Central Council (1995) *PREP and You: Card 3 Your Professional Development.* UKCC, London

2

Introduction and background to macro approaches

The starting point has to be why do organisations have a role in relation to the individuals' training and development needs? A clear response needs to be given to this question, when personal development has been perceived primarily as the responsibility of individuals themselves (Walters, 1995).

The co-dependants of the organisation and the individual is critical. To survive, an organisation must ensure that appropriate systems are in place which support individual development as an integral component of organisational goals.

Although individuals need to accept this responsibility, the organisation also has to ensure that systems are in place to support individual development in line with organisational goals. As is often stated organisational development can only occur through people development. This is highlighted by Tom Peters (1982) who, when discussing Disney's' success, stated, *'it all comes from people'*.

The organisation therefore cannot ignore its responsibility in developing individuals, if it wishes to succeed and continue to grow. In addition there are a number of contextual issues which are also driving this need for organisations' to ensure that systems are in place. These will be discussed below, firstly by concentrating on the NHS and nursing in particular, followed by a general review of issues relating to organisations and learning.

Nursing and the NHS

Nursing represents the largest and as such most expensive resource in the NHS. The National Audit Office in 1992, highlighted at that time that the NHS employed 400,000 nurses at a cost of £5 billion per year. Post registration education and training is recognised as fundamental to producing a quality health service (Bamford, 1997a). The costs of this provision are however obviously high, due to the large numbers of staff involved. In 1995 £756 million was spent on the provision of non-medical education in the United Kingdom (NHSE, 1995). Although this includes paramedics, and physiotherapists, nursing represents the largest proportion of staff within this expenditure. There is therefore a need to ensure that this public expenditure is targeted appropriately.

This need for continuing education is set against a background of changing healthcare needs, due to many external factors. Some of these include:

- technology: advances in healthcare, due to improved technology and pharmaceutical advances has led to a changing focus in healthcare provision, including increasing day surgery, a decreasing length of patient stay in hospitals and a continuing drive towards a primary led NHS (NHSE, 1996)
- demographics: people are now living longer with subsequent more complex healthcare needs. (WHPF, 1992)
- socio-economic climate: this in turn has had an effect on the economics of healthcare (Begg *et al,* 1994), with an increasing focus on the quality and effectiveness of care (DoH, 1995; DoH, 1996; DoH, 1997).

These issues have often resulted in changes in the roles and responsibilities for the groups below that are associated with development needs. These include:

- nurse practitioner roles (Coopers and Lybrand, 1996; Ashburner, 1997; Briggs, 1997)
- community nursing (Hancock, 1997)
- practice nursing (Smy, 1997)
- midwifery (Savage, 1994; Cameron, 1996; White, 1997)
- health visiting (Willis, 1997)
- support workers (Redfern, 1994; NHSE, 1995; Needham, 1996).

These have resulted in a need for continuous change. The Department of Health (DoH), recognising this stated in 1993 that a wide variety of instruments, education, training, retraining and research must be focused on a common objective — change within continuity.

Within nursing this need for continuous learning has not always been recognised. Jarvis (1987) stated that nursing should be viewed as a lifelong process requiring ongoing learning. In reality this was not always the case, many nurses once qualified did not necessarily continue to see learning as ongoing, where off the job learning activities tended to focus on training which was only associated with current tasks and psychomotor skills rather than forward planning (Hyland, 1997).

This focus has however shifted in the nineties. Changes in pre registration nurse education, following the reforms initiated by the Project 2000 report (UKCC, 1986). This resulted in provision within higher educational establishments, a minimum of diploma level qualification, and a move away from the historical apprenticeship type training. More recently there is a drive by professional bodies such as the Royal College of Nursing, for a graduate based profession. This has obviously had implications for those already qualified. Bamford (1997b), states that all nurses need to acquire academic attainment — to enable a greater ability to think, reason, argue and negotiate for the benefit of patients and clients. This achievement of academic attainment has been assisted by the introduction of a more flexible approach to the recognition of learning via systems such as Credit Accumulation and Transfer (CAT) schemes, Accreditation of Prior Learning (APL), and Accreditation of Experiential Learning (APEL) (Lillyman and Evans, 1996).

Alongside these drivers, as stated above, the professional body for nursing, The United Kingdom Central Council (UKCC) for Nurses, Midwives and Health Visitors, supports the need for continuous professional development and the need to maintain competence in both its *Code of Professional Conduct* (UKCC, 1992) and the *Post Registration Education and Practice Project (PREPP) Report* (UKCC, 1990).

The latter report resulted in a requirement that all nurses who wish to remain on the register must produce evidence of their ability and competence to practise. As part of this, all nurses must also keep a professional development profile, which may be utilised by the UKCC in the assessment of the completion of the PREPP requirements (UKCC, 1990). In addition over the 3 year intervals between registration periods nurses must demonstrate evidence of attendance at 5 study days or be able to demonstrate alternative equivalent learning processes. This reflects the individual accountability that nurses hold as part of the *Code of Professional Conduct* (UKCC, 1992). Extracts from this code state:

> *As a registered nurse, midwife or health visitor, you are personally accountable for your practice, and in the exercise of your professional accountability, must:*
>
> *Clause 3: Maintain and improve your professional knowledge and competence.*
>
> *Clause 4: Acknowledge any limitations in your knowledge and competence and decline any duties or responsibilities unless able to perform them in a safe and skilled manner.*
>
> *Clause 14: Assist professional colleagues, in the context of your own knowledge, experience and sphere of responsibility, to develop their professional competence, and assist others in the care team, including informal carers, to contribute safely and to a degree appropriate to their roles.*

More recently in 1995, the UKCC stated that in order for each employee to develop the required philosophy of lifelong learning, organisations themselves must have a commitment to education and training. As Moores (1984) and Davies (1990) state however, we cannot afford to waste any resources, therefore systems must be in place to identify how the needs of individuals and the organisation can be met.

In reality, however as Bamford (1997b) states, it became clear in the early 1990's that there were no accurate or robust mechanisms for costing education and training, never mind identifying whether these actually reflected need. This supports the findings of the English National Board's (a subsidiary of the UKCC) national training needs analysis, in

1990. This found that existing continuing education was *'uncoordinated, frequently repetitive, and often difficult for practitioners to access'*. As an example they found that less than 1 in 5 practitioners held a post registration qualification for the area in which they were working.

This latter research resulted in the production of a document *Framework for Continuing Education for Nurses, Midwifes and Health Visitors* (1991), which amongst other suggestions states that the future organisation of continuing education should:

- link education to quality of care, via ongoing performance review systems
- meet practitioners' needs via planned professional development based on the identification of organisational and individual needs.

Shepherd (1993), focused on the identification of training needs in qualified nurses. He found that, although the identification and satisfaction of need should be seen as a cyclic event within organisations and within the professionals' role, in reality this was not the case. He found little evidence of performance review being undertaken and no evidence of a systematic approach to the identification of need at that time.

More recently changes in the commissioning of Non-Medical Education (NHSE, 1995a), has resulted in an increasing focus on the local definition of training and development needs. There is a need therefore to ensure that robust systems are in place which identify organisational and individual needs.

These issues in nursing are set against the broader issues relating to learning and organisations which will be discussed in the next section.

Organisations and learning

Within management texts and the human resource management (HRM) literature, the virtues of developing individuals is continually stated. The National Economic Development Office in 1987 stated that *'People are a major source of competitive advantage'*. Sisson (1994) reiterates this, focusing on that how organisations recruit, train, reward, motivate and discipline their employees is of central importance to business success.

This is reflected in current drivers for organisations to be accredited with the *Investors in People* (IIP) award (NHSE, 1995b)

There are however a number of issues which may prevent this happening in reality. Examples include:

- Costs and perceived lack of immediacy of benefits. Pfeffer (1995) states in the short term the costs may be seen as prohibitive (on which most managers are measured), whereas the actual benefits may be seen either in the long term, or be accrued by another organisation if staff move. This latter issue has relevance for nursing, particularly since the advent of NHS Trusts. Nurses are very much a national workforce, often moving between individual Trusts, and therefore needing transferable skills. Managers however, are measured in the short term, often on a financial cost basis. There could therefore be a danger that nurses are not developed in the short term, resulting in a shortage of particular skills in the future.
- The decentralisation of management responsibilities, including training and development could also exacerbate this problem (Sisson, 1994).

As organisations become leaner and flatter (as is happening within the NHS), Kabst *et al* (1996), suggest that there is a need to change approaches to learning and development. They state there is a need for:

- permanent learning
- broad range of functions
- move away from tasks to competency based expectations of performance
- functional flexibility
- continuous learning
- on the job experiential learning.

They therefore believed that as organisations become leaner

there is a greater need to concentrate on focused ongoing development. The latter reflects current drives towards continuous development and the learning organisation, based on recent theories of how adults learn.

The learning organisation is defined by Pedler *et al* (1989) as:

> *an organisation which facilitates the learning of all of its members and continuously transforms itself.*

This focus on transformation rather than adaptation has been reiterated by Jones and Hendry (1994), who state that previous training has focused on enabling people to constantly adapt eg. learning new skills in relation to new tasks. With the continuous change process, decentralisation of management, and moves toward changes in management style, including greater worker participation following the Total Quality Management (TQM) movement, continuous learning and learning on the job have been given greater emphasis. The latter has been described as 'tacit knowledge' (Jones and Hendry, 1994). This is hidden learning when individuals acquire and develop skills and knowledge in the course of actually doing the job, and which is the result of experiential learning. According to Jones and Hendry (1994), the focus of the learning organisation should therefore be expanding and building on that which remains undeveloped.

As stated earlier, part of this need to change the way we look at learning within organisations, has arisen from changes in the way work is organised. As Sisson (1994) described , this is a move away from the traditional task based view of work, where people had different knowledge and skills in different functional areas and to this need for more flexible workers as described above. Reid *et al* (1992), state that this has resulted in individuals needing to *'learn how to learn'*, rather than having training which is content orientated .

This is also part of the drive towards individuals taking responsibility for their own learning. Knowles in 1980, stated that adults learn best when taking responsibility, when learning is self directed, and that they learn more through experiential learning.

This change in attitude towards learning in organisations

has been driven by various adult learning theories. Examples of which are those surrounding action learning (Lewin 1951), reflective learning (Schon, 1983; Kolb, 1984), and Knowles (1980) concept of experiential learning, amongst others. These theories have proven to be very influential in the development of individual and organisational learning, and indeed are promoted within the field of nursing (Morton-Cooper and Palmer, 1993), particularly in the process of reflection on practice (Palmer *et al*, 1992).

This obviously has implications for how individuals develop. Senge (1990) stated that individuals need to develop *'personal mastery'*. He goes on to describe this as:

> *The discipline of continually clarifying and deepening our personal vision, focusing our energies, and of seeing reality objectively*

The above is very much an individualistic view of learning, assuming responsibility is owned by self. This supports Wood's (1988) view of continuous learning and development. He states that individuals can, and should, create their own definitions of continuous development. Reid *et al* (1992) state however that a key trigger within any definition is the attitude to learning and that it must be believed by individuals to be a continuous process and not a series of one-off, disjointed activities that have an ending.

Other authors stress the organisations' role in continuous development and learning. Cooper and Signe (1978), and Jarvis (1992), identify the need for organisations to create a work climate conducive to learning and systems which encourage lifelong learning. This debate between individual and organisational responsibility for learning is continued by Senge (1990) who stated that an organisation's commitment to and capacity for learning can be no greater than its members, relating back to the earlier concept of personal mastery.

Bamford (1997b) argues however that this argument is a circular one, in that an organisation that values its members, and encourages their development is likely to be an organisation that thrives and develops, demonstrating the interrelationship between individual and organisational responsibility.

Sheperd (1993) states however, that unless individuals acknowledge the importance of continuous learning a dependency can be created between learners and providers, whereby others are expected to provide. Reid *et al* (1992) state there is a need therefore to create a set of balances between:

- learner dependency and independency
- standard programme delivery and unique self-directed plans
- learning and work viewed as separate processes and learning and work viewed as an integrated whole.

There appears therefore to be a dual responsibility for learning within organisations. The individual must be involved, and take responsibility for their learning, however the organisation must ensure systems are in place to support the concepts of reflection, learning to learn and experiential learning.

There is therefore a need to focus on not only macro approaches to the identification of and responsibility for learning, for example IPR and training strategies, but also systems which encourage the individual responsibility, for example profiling and reflection on practice (referred to as micro approaches) the latter of which will be discussed in detail in section two.

In addition there is a need for multifaceted systems which:

- encourage individual involvement yet reflect organisational goals and targets
- are continuous, reflecting learning theory
- are systematic
- encourage experiential learning
- take into account accrediting previous learning systems AP(E)L
- ensure effective use of resource for both individuals and organisations.

Potential approaches will be discussed in the next chapter.

References

Ashburner L (1997) Defining role *Health Serv J* 17th July, **107**(5562): 32–3

Bamford M (1997a) Funding issues in education and training. In: Morton-Cooper A, Bamford M eds. (1997) *Excellence in healthcare Management*. Blackwell, Oxford

Bamford M (1997b) Health careers in the 21st century. In: Morton-Cooper A, Bamford M eds. (1997) *Excellence in healthcare Management*. Blackwell, Oxford

Begg D, Fischer S, Dornbusch R (1994) *Economics 4th ed* McGraw-Hil, England

Briggs M (1997) Developing nursing role *Nurs Standard* 28th May **11**(36): 49–55

Cameron J (1996) The changing childbirth contacts register. *MIDIRS Midwifery Digest*. June 1996 **6**(2):144

Cooper S, Signe S (1978) Continuing education. In: Popiel ES ed. (1978) *Nursing and the Process of Continuing Education.* CV Mosby, St. Louis

Coopers and Lybrand (1996) *Nurse Practitioner Evaluation Project*. NHSE, London

Davies C (1990) *The Collapse of the Conventional Career. The Future of Work and its Relevance for Post Registration Education in Nursing, Midwifery and Health Visiting. Project Paper One*. English National Board Report, London

Department of Health (1995) *Improving the Effectiveness of Clinical Services*. HMSO, London.

Department of Health (1996) *The National Health Service. A Service with Ambitions*. HMSO, London.

Department of Health (1997) *The New NHS: Modern, Dependable*. HMSO, London

ENB (1990) *Framework for Continuing Education and Training for Nurses, Midwives And Health Visitors: Project Paper Two Summary Report for Managers*. ENB, London

ENB (1991) *Framework for Continuing Professional Education for Nurses, Midwives And Health Visitors. Guide to Implementation*. ENB, London

Hancock C (1997) Stand by for super nurses. *Health Serv J* 9th Jan **107**(5535):17

Hyland T (1997) A critique of alternative pathways in professional and vocational education. In: Morton-Cooper A, Bamford M eds. (1997) *Excellence in healthcare Management*. Blackwell, Oxford

Jarvis P (1992) Quality in practice: the role of education, *Nurse Education Today* **12:** 3–10

Jones AM, Hendry C (1994) The learning organisation: adult learning and organisational transformation. *Bri J of Management* **5**: 153-162

Kabst R, Holt Larsen H, Branning P (1996) How do lean management organisations behave regarding training and development. *The Intnl J of HRM* 7:3 Set. 1996:618:639

Knowles MS (1980) *The Modern Practice of Adult Education: From Pedagogy to Andragogy*. Cambridge Books, New York

Kolb DA (1984) *Experiential Learning: Experience as the source of learning and development.* Prentice Hall, New Jersey

Lewin K (1951) *Field Theory in Social Science*. Haper Row, New York

Lillyman S, Evans B (1996) *Designing a Personal Portfolio/Profile.* Quay Books, Mark Allen Publishing, Dinton

Moores Y (1984) Release and provision for continuing education. *Nurse Education Today* **4**(11): 22–4

Morton-Cooper A, Palmer A (1993) *Mentoring and Preceptorship*. Blackwell, Oxford

National Economic Development Office/ Manpower Services Commission (1987) *People: The Key to Success*. NEDO, London

Needham J (1996) Balancing skill mix-future paediatric healthcare provision, *J of Nursing Management* May 1996 **4**(3):127–31

NHSE (1995a) *Education and Training in the New NHS EL (95)27* National Health Service Executive, London

NHSE (1995b) *Building on the benefits of occupational and national vocational qualifications in the NHS EL (95) 84.* National Health Service Executive, London

NHSE (1996) *Priorities and Planning Guidance for the NHS 1997-98.* National Health Service Executive, London

Palmer A, Burns S, Bulman C (1992) *Reflective Practice in Nursing.* Blackwell, Oxford

Peters T (1982) *In Search of Excellence.* Video New York

Pedler M, Boydell T, Burgoyne J (1989) Towards the learning company. *Management Education and Development* **20**

Pfeffer J (1995) *Competitive Advantage Through People: Unleashing the Power of the Workforce.* Harvard Business School Press, Boston

Redfern L (1994) Healthcare assistants: the challenge for nursing staff. *Nurs Times* 30th Nov **90**(48):31–3

Reid MA, Barrington H, Kenney J (1992) *Training Interventions. Managing Employee Development.* IPM, London

Savage W (1994) Changing childbirth, *Midwifes Chronicle* Nov 1994 **107**(1282): 411–13

Schon DA (1983) *The Reflective Practitioner. How Professionals think in action.* Basic Books, New York

Senge PM (1990) *The Fifth Discipline: The Art and Practice of the Learning Organisation.* Century Press, London

Sheperd JC (1993) *Training Needs Analysis of qualified nurse practitioners across three health authorities.* Unpublished PhD Thesis, University of Birmingham

Sisson K (1994) *Personnel Management.* Blackwell, Oxford

Smy J (1997) Nurses ring the changes. *Practice Nurse* 7th March **13**(4): 181–2

United Kingdom Central Council (1986) *Project 2000: A new preparation for practice.* UKCC, London

United Kingdom Central Council (1990) *The Report of Post Registration, Education and Practice Project (PREPP Report)* UKCC, London

United Kingdom Central Council (1992) *Code of Professional Conduct.* UKCC, London

United Kingdom Central Council (1995) *Implementation of the UKCC's Standards for Post Registration Education and Practice (PREP)* UKCC, London

Walters M (1995) *The Performance Management Handbook.* Insitutie of Personnel and Devleopment, London

White C (1997) Think-tank questions benefits of midwife-led model of maternity care. *Health Serv J* 13th Feb **107**(5540): 7

WHPF (1992) *Health and Social Care 2010.* Welsh Health Planning Forum, Cardiff

Willis J (1997) Health Visiting: which way forward. *Nurs Times* 22nd Oct **93**(43):56–7

Wood S (1988) *Continuous Development: the Path to Improved Performance.* IPM, London

3

Macro approaches to the identification of development needs

When considering a macro approach to the identification of training needs, it is necessary to consider the organisational role rather than focusing specifically on the individual. This does not mean that an individualistic approach cannot be taken. Rather that the responsibility at macro level is to establish the appropriate systems which focus on looking at the whole, the interaction between its independent parts. This concept is taken from social systems theory and will be utilised in the following sections when considering the macro rather than micro approach. The latter will be discussed in the second part of the book. (For a useful discussion of social systems theory, including its limitations please see Gharajedaghi and Ackoff in Tsoukas, 1994)

This short chapter therefore gives an overview of the macro approaches identifying need by first considering social systems theory as a foundation, before considering examples of this in action in the form of strategic planning and performance management systems. This will be broken down into organisational, departmental and individual levels and highlight the various approaches that can be taken to identify need at the various levels.

The practical details of implementation will then be discussed in *Chapter 4*.

Systems theory

A system can be defined as something that functions by virtue of its interdependent parts interacting with each other, often on feedback mechanisms, an example being the human body. In addition to this internal focus, organisational systems have been defined as being open and not closed systems. They must interact with their environment in order to survive (Huczynski and Buchanan, 1991).

Many management systems and techniques are based on this concept, for example strategic planning, and performance management systems, both of which are discussed in more detail below.

Strategic planning

Macro approaches should be based on a longer term strategic view and linked to the overall organisational business strategy or objectives. This is to ensure that individuals within the organisation have the required skills and /or knowledge base to meet the requirements of future roles within the organisation. Defining the organisational training strategy is also based on the same principles of strategic planning, and will be discussed in more detail in *Chapter 4* when an individual approach will be discussed in depth.

Having a longer term strategy is not sufficient however, if performance management systems do not exist, as the strategy needs to be reflected in departmental and individual performance expectations.

Performance management

Figure 3.1 is a performance management model demonstrating the concept of feedback systems in social systems theory.

The premise of this model is that organisational objectives/targets should be reflected downwards into defined departmental objectives which are then identified within individual targets, either outcome based (in the form of objectives/targets), or process based (in the form of expected levels of performance for example job descriptions/ competencies).

Via a performance measurement process, such as Individual Performance Review, gaps in performance may then identify learning needs both of individuals and departments. Alternative forms of measurement may be utilised including formal auditing systems such as Bench-marking, Kings Fund Organisational Audit or Investors in People. These can identify deficits in performance. These tend however to focus on systems at organisational level and do not always identify individual needs.

As shown in *Figure 3.1* performance management can be considered at 3 levels these being: Organisational Departmental and Individual Levels. This is explained further in the sections below.

Figure 3.1: Individual and Organisational Learning Needs Based on the Performance Management Cycle

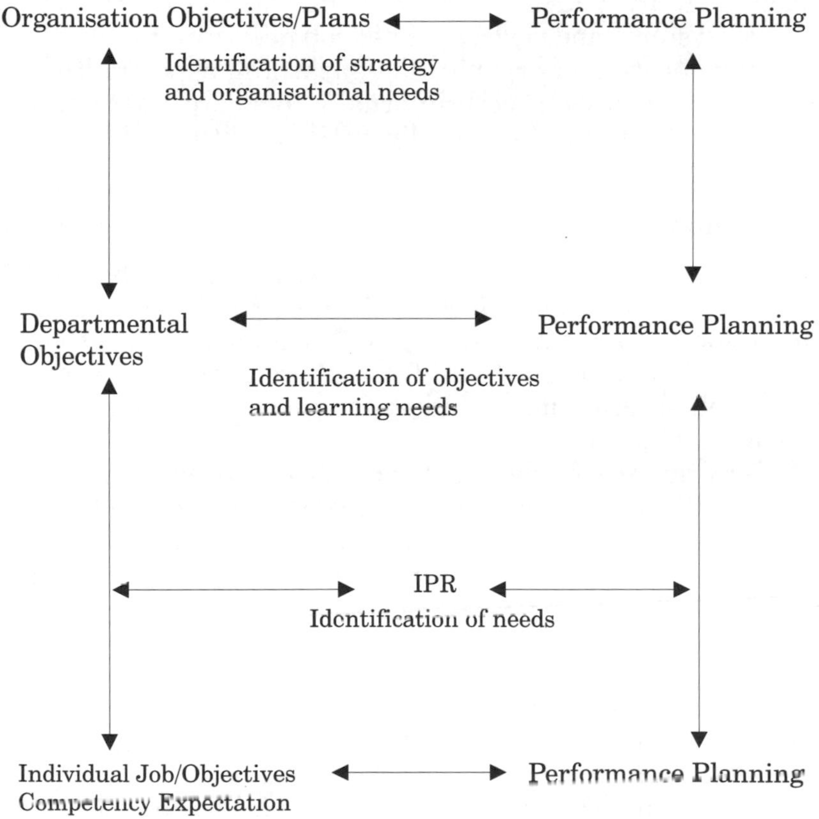

Organisational level

As stated earlier, at organisational level there is obviously a need to drive the process by having a clearly defined strategy or business plan. This should identify what the organisation is about, who its customers are, and how it intends to do business. This should then be demonstrated by clear objectives and action plans.

At organisational level various approaches can then be utilised to identify learning and development needs. This should be part of an organisation's training and development strategy. Part of this strategy could be to undertake an organisational training needs analysis, and ensure that systems are in place for performance management, for example Individual Performance Review (IPR), effective grading systems and clearly defined job descriptions.

Identification of organisational learning opportunities at this level is also vital, both internally eg. career structures, in-house training, and externally eg. links with local learning institutions.

Departmental level

At this level the organisational strategy should then be turned into departmental objectives. A departmental training plan can be formulated which should reflect information gathered from the IPR process. In addition there may be a need to review job descriptions and identify specific competencies for various staff roles.

Performance Review is often advocated as a means of bridging the gap between organisational and individual development, a major objective of the system also being to identify training needs at both individual and departmental level (Armstrong, 1991; Kinnie and Lowe, 1990; Bevan and Thompson, 1991).

More recently there has also been a move towards competency based approaches, which can be utilised for measuring performance, identifying gaps in competence and hence a training need.

Each of these processes can therefore feed into each other. For example competencies can be used within the IPR process, information from which can then develop the departmental training plan. This demonstrates the double loop feedback process of systems theory.

It may occasionally also be appropriate to undertake a specific training needs analysis across the department, to gain a snapshot of needs at that time.

As at the organisational level, learning opportunities at departmental level also need defining, both internally and externally, and on and off the job.

Individual level

From a macro perspective the organisation has a role in ensuring that systems are in place to define learning and development needs at the individual level.

This may include the definition of appropriate individual standards required, which enable the organisational objectives to be met through individual participation and performance management systems. Examples of these standards include individual job descriptions and competency requirements. There may be a need to ensure that these reflect the various components of the required competencies. For example the individual role may need clarifying as to not only what knowledge base is required , but also the skills element and expected values and beliefs inherent in the role (Ward, 1993).

This will then enable the appropriate definition of development needs, to ensure that this is not only targeted at academic or skills based learning .

In addition, to ensure effective involvement of individuals, the organisation has a role in ensuring that effective two way communication systems exist and that individuals can then feedback into the planning process, thereby bridging organisational and individual planning and development needs.

In reality if the systems approach is taken too literally, it can have its limitations.

Within performance review for example there are potential conflicts within the process itself. Bevan and Thompson (1991) state that in order to demonstrate a need the individual may feel that they are acknowledging a weakness. Kinnie and Lowe (1990) state that this is the classic *'coach/judge'* dilemma that managers face in managing performance.

Reinforcing the earlier discussion Shepherd (1993), also stated that for this system to work effectively there must be explicit aims/objectives against which the performance of the practitioner and the organisation may be measured. These aims/goals may then however, be seen as purely organisationally driven and may not be owned by individuals.

Organisations, therefore, may wish to ensure that alternative systems exist alongside the performance review process to encapsulate the individuality and often personal needs of their staff, which can then be utilised in defining organisational needs and development. An example of this type of process is Personal Development Profiling (IPD, 1995) or as introduced in one health organisation — career profiling (Ward and Lillyman, 1996; Ward, 1997).

The details of this approach will be discussed in *Chapter 7*, however again from a macro view, the organisation still has a responsibility to ensure that the appropriate systems and support are established.

The practicalities of introducing macro approaches will now be discussed in the next chapter.

References

Armstrong M (1991) *A Handbook of Personnel Management Practice 4th ed.* Kogan Page, London

Bevan S, Thompson M (1991) Performance management at the crossroads. *Personnel Management* Nov 1991

Gharajedaghi J, Ackoff RL (1994) Mechanisms, organisms, and social systems. In: Tsoukas H (1994) *New Thinking in Organisational Behaviour*. Butterworth Heinemann, Oxford

Huczynski A, Buchanan D (1991) *Organizational Behaviour*. Prentice Hall, London

Institute of Personnel and Development (1995) CPD package launch *People Management* 5th October 1995

Kinnie N, Lowe D (1990) Performance related pay on the shopfloor. *Personnel Management* Nov 1990

Shepherd JC (1993) *Training Needs Analysis of qualified nurse practitioners across three health authorities.* Unpublished PhD Thesis, University of Birmingham

Ward C (1993) Overcoming potential dissonance between organisational and individual development needs. In: Management development and the changing role of the ward manager. *J Nurs Management* Supplement 1 **1**

Ward C, Lillyman S (1996) CV Times—a system of career profiling for individual qualified nurses. *Health Service Journal.* April 4th **106**(5497): 31

Ward C (1997) *An exploration of Macro v Micro approaches to identifying the training and development needs of qualified nursing staff.* Unpublished MBA Thesis. University of Warwick

4

How to identify training and development needs

This chapter focuses on how the organisation can identify training and development needs. Practical examples are given, relating back to the theoretical context in the previous chapter.

The first section concentrates on how to develop a training and development strategy, discussing in detail how to identify the external and internal issues affecting the organisation and individuals. How to undertake a SWOT (strengths, weaknesses, opportunities and threats) analysis. How to identify priorities, objectives, action plans and resource requirements. Practical examples are given in the appendices.

Section two discusses how managers and individuals can identify both external and internal learning opportunities. Approaches to undertaking a training needs analysis are then discussed in section three, including competency definition, questionnaires, interviews, focus groups and marginal analysis. Again practical examples are given in the appendices. The final section concentrates on individual performance review systems, including a discussion of what can go wrong and how this can be overcome.

Developing a training and development strategy

The strategic planning process described below can be utilised when developing any strategy. In this context however the focus will be on developing a training and development strategy. *Figure 4.1* illustrates this in more detail.

Figure 4.1: The strategic planning process

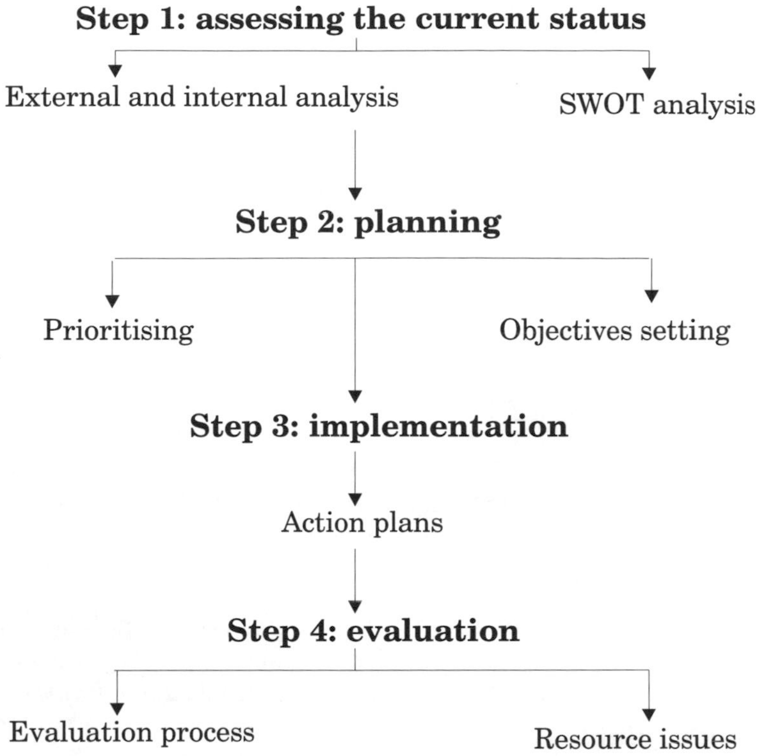

Most strategic planning processes follow the basic components of problem solving. That is the stages of assessment, planning, implementation and evaluation.

In this context the initial stage of assessing the current context and status is vital. The earlier discussion relating to organisations as open social systems must be considered to understand why it is essential to ensure that not only do we assess the internal organisational status, but also that we consider the external environment in which it functions.

Assessment then should consider a review of the external and internal issues surrounding training and development, followed by an evaluation of its strengths, weaknesses, opportunities and threats: a SWOT Analysis.

Reviewing external and internal issues

A useful model for considering the external environment is shown in *Figure 4.2*.

Figure 4.2: reviewing the external environment

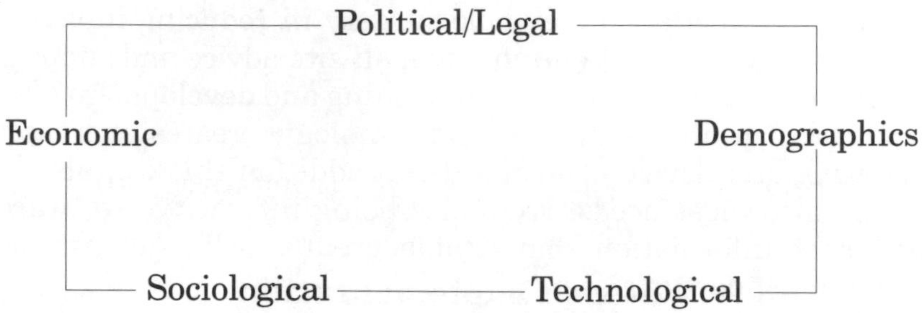

In relation to training and development for example the following may need to be considered.

Political/legal

What current government or professional policies are currently, or will potentially, affect the organisation? Examples of these in this context are those cited in *Chapter 2* .

Demographics

How will demographic changes affect either healthcare needs, the provision of care, and/or the demographics of those who provide care? For example in respect of the latter issue — within the nursing professions, concerns have been expressed regarding the number of expected retirees by the year 2000.

Economics

How will the economics of healthcare affect the provision of care, and hence changing needs in respect of roles, skill mix issues and development needs?

What are the issues to balance between financial cost and quality costs?

Sociological

What changes are occurring in society that have an impact on care? Examples being changing disease patterns, an increasing focus on health promotion, and changing public expectations.

Technological

How is technology changing healthcare provision? For example, the effect of key hole surgery in reducing inpatient stay, telecommunications enabling off site advice and support. What impact has technology on training and development? For example, in itself increasing technology creates increased training and development needs, in addition this can also be utilised to meet needs. Examples being interactive software, Internet information that enable greater self and distance learning opportunities.

The internal environment

A suggested model for reviewing the internal environment is shown below as *Figure 4.3*.

Figure 4.3: reviewing the internal environment

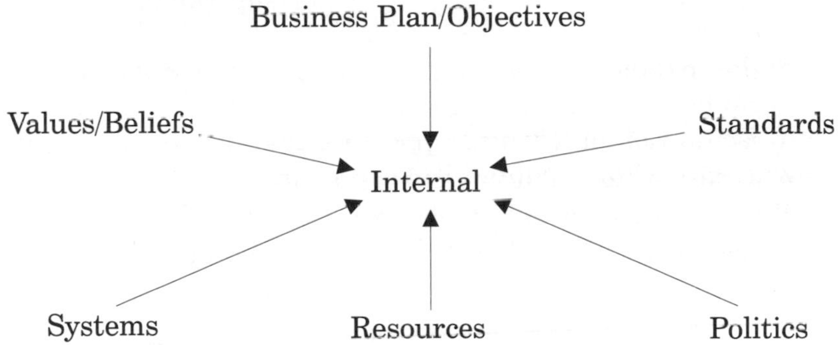

Business plans/objectives

What are the major issues within the business plan or organisational objectives, that may have implications for training and development? For example, are there plans to change service delivery which change resource requirements in terms not only of numbers of staff required, but also the skill mix, and development needs?

Are there changes in local policies which have an impact on future requirements? For example, if there is a move to provide nurse led services what impact will this have, not only on the need to produce specialist practitioners, but also the impact on the generalists? Will the pool of generalist nurses be diminished? Will there be a need to consider alternative forms of provision, for example healthcare assistants/support workers. Or will there be a need to liaise with local education consortium regarding the need to recruit more pre-registration students (if possible)?

This link between the business planning process and organisational development reinforces the principles of performance management demonstrated in *Figure 3.1.* Unfortunately however, in many organisations they are seen as independent, with less attention paid to resource planning and the identification of training and development needs.

Values/Beliefs

The culture of the organisation and the values and beliefs that exist in relation to training and development cannot be ignored. There is a need therefore to consider values/beliefs in relation to:

- the balance between psychomotor and cognitive skills
- facilitation of learning opportunities
- experiential and academic opportunities
- internal v external provision
- organisational and individual responsibility
- forms of assessment of knowledge/skills eg. accreditation v non-accreditation
- resource commitment direct eg. immediate financial and indirect costs eg. time
- balance of theory and practice
- levels of competence required
- mandatory Vs voluntary participation.

Politics

Alongside the above there is a need to consider internal politics in terms of the balance between centralised and decentralised functions and responsibilities. Tensions may exist if these are not clearly defined. In relation to training and development the performance management model utilised earlier assumes that information gathered at departmental/individual level can feedback into organisational strategy. In reality the authors' experience is that either this information is not systematically collected or that departmental managers assume that a centralised function such as the personnel department should be responsible. The same tensions may then exist in relation to the provision of training and development .

While there has been a move towards flatter organisational structures and decentralisation of functions, at the same time there is often a need to ensure that there is still corporate cohesion and overall strategic direction.

This then involves a fine balance between the need to centralise some functions and provide a supporting network while ensuring that managers at local level not only have the power to make decisions, but also have been personally developed to assume this responsibility. In addition these managers must also have their performance measured and be held to account.

In this context for example, the identification and addressing of training and development needs should be a middle manager's responsibility, with a supporting centralised infrastructure. In reality, the authors experience in a number of organisations, is that many middle managers have not been prepared for their roles, the demarcation lines between centralised and decentralised functions have not been clearly drawn, and systems do not exist to support the core functions. This often then accumulates into departmental tensions and a blame culture.

It is imperative therefore that the internal assessment acknowledges any tensions that exist because of the internal political scenario and identifies the underlying cause rather than the superficial problems.

Systems

There is a need to identify the status of the current systems in place that assist in ongoing performance management and identification of training and development needs. Questions that may need to be asked in relation to the IPR system for example include:

- is the process standardised across the organisation?
- what is used for baseline measurement? Is this in the form of objectives or competencies?
- what standards exist in terms of how regular is the process?

The above will be discussed in more detail later under the heading 'Individual performance review systems'. In addition there is a need to assess:

- what organisational and local policies and protocols exist in relation to the identification and meeting of development needs? For example is there equity in secondment policies across the organisation?
- are there established information systems which capture data relating to training and development needs? Examples being either electronic or manual databases which may exist in the form of simple training files.

Standards

Again there is a need to identify what standards exist currently in the organisation that clearly outline expectations of performance, and how this is then measured?

For example are these expectations based on traditional organisational job descriptions or are there defined competencies?

Whatever form of standards exist how are these measured? Is there a formal IPR system as previously discussed? Are there current forms of assessment linked to formal accreditation systems? For example, academic programmes or National Vocational Qualifications (NVQ).

Resources

An internal assessment of resources needs to consider not only financial issues but also the less tangible considerations, examples include:

- what internal and external support systems exist to meet learning needs?
- what are the current relationships and access to internal and external providers?
- what are the current skills and knowledge base of staff employed? This may not always be known, and may demonstrate a need to undertake a systematic training needs analysis (TNA), which will be discussed in more detail later
- what learning opportunities exist within and external to the organisation question? As this is an area where many managers have highlighted gaps in knowledge base, this will be discussed in more detail later.

This initial assessment of internal and external issues is therefore critical and should not be rushed before considering the way forward. In addition when reviewing these issues it must be with a long term view. That is we must consider not only the current issues affecting the organisation, but also the potential impact of future changes. For example planned changes in service delivery in three to five years time may impact on resource planning, skill mix and hence changes in potential skills/knowledge requirements.

An example of an Acute Trusts External and Internal Issues is included in *Appendix I.*

SWOT Analysis

The next stage of the assessment stage is to assess the organisation's strengths weaknesses, opportunities and threats.

Strengths and weaknesses that may be considered in relation to:

- financial assets eg the environment, internal resource

- human assets eg. people, skills, teamwork, leadership styles
- systems eg. communication, IPR etc.
- relationships
- culture and internal political status.

What opportunities or threats are presented by:

- new legislation?
- purchasers of service?
- changes in healthcare ?
- other providers of service?
- professional bodies?

When undertaking a SWOT analysis, it is not always possible to compartmentalise issues, for example strengths may also be weaknesses, opportunities may also present a threat.

The underlying principle however is that future objectives should build on the strengths, address the weaknesses, seize the opportunities while managing the risk of the threats.

An example of an Acute Trusts SWOT analysis is included in *Appendix II*.

Prioritising and objective setting

The above assessment often highlights a number of needs which may seem impossible to address. There is therefore a need to undertake a prioritising exercise.

A simple approach to consider, is what must be addressed compared to what should and what do you want to.

The identification of objectives and action plans in relation to the former priorities, and acknowledgement of resources required to achieve them, often results in a recognition that other issues may have to be addressed at a later date.

Objectives should then be defined which broadly state what must and should be achieved. Although wherever possible these should be measurable with expected time-scales, this definition of measurable outcomes may be more appropriate in the identification of specific action plans against each objective which can then be used in the evaluation stage.

Action planning

Action plans relating to each objective should be explicit in terms of defining what needs doing, how this will be achieved, who is responsible for ensuring achievement of the action, and when this needs to be done by. Each objective may require either a single or a number of action plans.

Implementation of the strategy should then follow from the action plans. An example of an Acute Trusts objectives/action plans is included in *Appendix III*.

Resource identification and the evaluation process

In order to complete the strategic planning process, it is important to identify the potential resources required, not only in terms of financial resource, but also in terms of time required and thereby ensure that the strategy is realistic. In addition the evaluation process must be defined within the initial strategy. This may be in its most simplistic form, ie. evaluation via individual performance review of the individual responsibilities for various actions.

A more systematic and effective approach is to have a group which ensures the implementation and evaluation of the strategy. Examples being the corporate team or a sub-branch of this eg. a training and development group. Whatever the group is called its responsibilities should be to continue to provide the strategic direction and corporate cohesiveness in ensuring that the objectives are achieved.

As shown in the performance management model this can then be reflected in departmental and individual objectives and expected achievements. In addition this model can also be used to identify local strategies.

There are a number of approaches mentioned above that now need exploring in more depth these include:

- how to identify learning opportunities
- systematic training needs analysis
- IPR systems.

Assessing current learning opportunities

Traditional views of learning opportunities tend to focus on potential attendance at various study days either internal or external which appear to relate to meeting a particular need.

For example, if an individual states that they are not comfortable with interviewing individuals, which may be either staff or patients, then often an appropriate study day or workshop on developing interviewing skills is sought. While not wishing to undermine the potential benefits of such an experience this section aims to identify that there are alternative ways of learning and developing. As stated earlier in *Chapter 2,* with the increasing recognition of experiential and reflective learning, various opportunities should be considered.

In the above example, alternative approaches could include, the individual observing an experienced confident interviewer in action, with the opportunity to then evaluate the interview reflecting on the learning points. In addition the individual could be observed, with feedback given after. Alternatively they could be asked to undertake a literature review identifying standards of good practice in interviewing and then be asked to undertake an audit of other interviewers, again given the opportunity to reflect on the process.

The identification of an individual's potential learning opportunities will be further explored later in the book. This section will be concentrating on the organisation or manager's role in identifying potential learning opportunities, both within and external to the organisation.

External opportunities

It is essential that managers are aware of the current opportunities available external to the organisation. Examples of which are listed below:

- Academic programmes: these are obviously multifaceted eg. diplomas, degrees, and professional programmes. As it is often difficult for individual managers to collect data relating to all available programmes however, the organisation should have a resource centre, which has up to date institutional prospectuses, and ideally an individual who can act as a resource/adviser.

- Accreditation systems: there are various forms of accreditation systems some of which such as APEL (Accreditation of experiential learning) and CATS (Credit accumulation and transfer scheme) are discussed in more detail in *Chapter 7*. Although all managers need to have an understanding of the principles of CATS and APEL and ideally have access to an adviser where required. In addition managers need to understand the NVQ (National Vocational Qualifications) framework, in order to make decisions as to the appropriateness of this approach in their area.
- National occupational standards: there are numerous occupational standards now available which can be utilised in performance management, or can be linked to the NVQ framework if accreditation is required. Examples being the care standards and the MCI (Management Charter Initiative) standards.
- Secondments: alternative external opportunities such as potential secondments should also be investigated by managers.
- Conferences: individuals may wish not only to attend specific conferences, but should be encouraged, if they have the knowledge and skill base, to present a paper or poster.
- Funding: problems often arise in relation to funding. There are however, a number of bursaries and awards available which should be explored.

Examples of potential sources are included in *Appendix IV*.

Internal opportunities

A number of learning opportunities can be explored internally these include:

- internal provision ie. what structured programmes are offered internally?

- secondment /shadowing: what opportunities exist for shadowing or to second individuals to other departments?
- project/audit work: are there potential projects or audits which could benefit the individual and the department?
- literature search: what potential literature search areas might individuals benefit from?
- job swap: is there potential for individuals to swap jobs for a given period of time?
- utilising local expertise/skills: are there individuals with specific skills who can enable individuals to learn on the job?
- journal clubs/special interest groups: are there in-house special interest groups/project teams or journal clubs which would benefit individuals? For example research interest groups, clinical effectiveness groups
- case studies: is there the potential for an individual to undertake a case study which could be presented to others?
- mentorship/preceptorship/clinical supervision: what support systems exist to facilitate learning? Would individuals themselves benefit from acting as a supervisor to others?
- funding: what financial resources are available internally? How does the application process for funding work?

Learning opportunities for individuals within organisations are therefore potentially vast. Individuals may not benefit however, if they and their managers are not aware of the potential. Managers need also to consider their own values and beliefs in relation to learning opportunities, considering the issues outlined earlier in this chapter.

Training needs analysis (TNA)

Before considering various approaches to the systematic identification of training needs it is useful to consider a definition of training need. Bashford (1991) states that a training need arises when knowledge or a skill are deficient, and in such cases, training intervention is required. From an organisational perspective this definition may not be sufficient however, as there may be a gap between the organisation's values and beliefs and the individual's. As well as considering knowledge and skills it is recommended therefore that the affective elements (ie. attitudes, values and beliefs) are also considered .

Also implicit in the definition is that the required knowledge/skills are identified .

This may be in the form of job descriptions, person specifications or, as we have seen more recently, standards of competence. Organisations therefore need to consider what they are using as their baseline for analysis. It may be necessary in the first instance to update job descriptions or define appropriate competency requirements, as discussed below.

Standards and competencies

The level to which these are defined is dependant on the individual organisation's need. There is a balance to be struck between quantifying (as much as is possible), standards, and ensuring practicality of use for ongoing performance management (PM) and identification of training needs.

For example, there are now occupational standards for many employment groups which are utilised within the National Vocational Qualification (NVQ) framework. Although these have been perceived as beneficial in defining core standards, identifying training needs and motivating employees, at the same time they have been criticised for the bureaucracy involved and potential rigidity (Beaumont Report, 1996).

Locally defined standards of competence may be required to enable ownership of standards and ensure greater flexibility. Organisations therefore need to consider the potential advantages of either adopting national standards or developing local ones. Each is considered in *Table 4.1*.

Table 4.1			
National		**Local**	
Advantages	Disadvantages	Advantages	Disadvantages
Developed by consortium eg. Care sector consortium Core standards Prevents duplication of effort Usually linked to formal accreditation	May not be flexible enough to meet local requirements Lack of local ownership May by too bureaucratic and unwieldy	Ownership Flexibility May be more practical or appropriate - local PM system	Duplication of effort Not linked to accreditation

Organisations may wish to consider either utilising national standards, adapting them to meet local needs or, developing local standards of competence internally. The latter can be produced by utilising working groups of appropriate stakeholders. An example of locally produced competencies are included in *Appendix V*. These G grade competencies were initially developed by the author at an acute hospital (Ward, 1993), and have subsequently been updated in a number of other organisations, by Ward Whitfield Associates while working in a consultancy capacity. In all cases G grades and managers undertook group work during a performance management workshop to produce initial concepts. These were then formalised, utilising a framework originally published by the Health Service Management Unit in the early 1990's relating to G grade competencies. The advantage of this approach is that these managers are more likely to accept the standards as part of a formal PM system.

Although competencies can be utilised from other organisations, in the authors experience, this internal development and debate surrounding the issues is a prerequisite for true ownership, and hence utilisation within the performance management framework.

Whatever form of training needs analysis is undertaken therefore, there is a need firstly to ensure that a baseline standard is available in order to identify any gaps.

Approaches to TNA

The choice of method is often dependant on many issues, these being:

- size of population and subsequent sample size
- the need to ensure appropriate representation (reliability) versus the need to ensure the method adequately identifies true needs (validity)
- the overall objectives of the TNA eg. there may be a need to ensure involvement of appropriate stakeholders, to ensure future ownership of recommendations
- quantitative versus qualitative approaches
- cost.

Different approaches to identification of need by systematic TNA will now be considered. Various approaches can be utilised including:

- questionnaires (McCelland, 1994a; Shepherd, 1993)
- interviews (McCelland, 1994b)
- focus groups (Ward, 1993; McCelland, 1994c)
- marginal analysis (Teasdale, 1992)
- a combination of approaches.

Questionnaires

Questionnaires can be very useful, particularly if larger samples of the population are required, in order to enable greater representation and/or future ownership of results. In addition they can be easier to administer, and less time consuming than other methods.

Disadvantages however include :

- less potential to gather qualitative data
- analysis can be difficult if open questions are used
- the lack of opportunity to check understanding, or to follow up any answers/comments

- less personal contact, which can result in a poor response rate
- user saturation: there has been a proliferation of questionnaires from all sources in recent times. This again can result in poor response rates.

In order to minimise the potential for the above, effective communication regarding the purpose/objectives of the survey is therefore essential. In addition careful consideration must be given to the following issues:

- questionnaire design
- piloting and distribution
- analysis.

Questionnaire design

Designing a questionnaire is not as easy as it first appears. As Oppenheim (1996) states:

> *the world is full of well meaning people who believe that anyone who can write plain English and has a modicum of common sense can produce a good questionnaire.*

Careful thought must be given to the type of questions to be utilised, the actual wording of individual questions, and the layout of the questionnaire (See *Appendix VI*).

In this technological age no Training Needs Analysis, using structured questionnaires should be done manually. There are many commercial software packages that can assist in the process. If you do not have the expertise it is important to enlist help at the design stage. If open questions are used there is a need to consider how the analysis will be undertaken manually. As stated above it is then essential to test out the analysis process within the pilot stage.

Interviews

The advantages of interviews in TNA are not only that more qualitative data can be collected, but that it offers a more adaptable approach than questionnaires do.

In an interview situation, responses to questions can be checked and followed up by further questions. An experienced interviewer can also observe non-verbal responses such as hesitation, facial expressions, and other body language, which may facilitate further questioning.

Disadvantages however include:

- subjectivity of approach, may result in interviewer bias
- time consuming and hence expensive
- may be smaller sample size which may not be representative
- interviewee may seek to please interviewer, in this personal contact situation resulting in bias
- data collection may be difficult
- analysis of data is often more difficult.

In order to minimise the above, as with questionnaires, the overall interview approach should be appropriate to the overall objectives to be achieved. Careful consideration however, should be given to the following:

- style of interview and types of questions
- bias minimisation
- data collection
- data analysis.

These are discussed in *Appendix VII*

Focus groups

Rather than individual interviews a useful approach that can be utilised in TNA is the use of representative focus groups. If the population size is not too big it may be possible to involve all participants by holding a number of groups. For example the author has utilised this approach when identifying the needs of all the G grade ward managers in an Acute hospital (Ward, 1993). Following distribution and analysis of a self assessment ranking questionnaire, group meetings were held for all G grades.

A semi-structured approach was used, whereby a presentation was given regarding the new Nursing Strategy, the questionnaire results and draft G Grade Competencies. A group discussion then took place regarding their overall perceived need.

The benefits of this type of approach are, that there is the opportunity to gather rich qualitative data, enable greater ownership of the project, and develop issues that arise from group brainstorming rather than individual reflection.

Disadvantages include:

- time and hence cost
- representation: in the example above, all of the population were included, however this is not always possible
- individuals may be influenced by, or not feel confident in, the group and may not give their opinion
- the facilitator must be experienced as this process is not easily managed.

This is however, a very useful approach if combined with another method eg. questionnaire or individual interviews.

Marginal analysis

Marginal analysis involves collecting data regarding current provision/status in comparison with organisational or individual targets. Discussion then takes place with significant players, usually managers, around the margins or gaps (Teasdale, 1992).

An example in relation to TNA, would be to compare data relating to numbers of nurses and midwives at certain grades who hold a particular qualification eg. the ENB 997/8 course. If a target had been set that all E grades and above should have this qualification, comparisons could be made with the actual numbers, and a discussion take place with managers regarding any gaps. Decisions could then be made as to future educational requirements or, if necessary to change the initial standard.

This approach obviously has advantages in that it should be fairly easy, quick and cost effective if efficient data collection systems exist. It can also yield objective, quantitative information which can be used for planning purposes and to enable future service negotiations both internally and externally.

Disadvantages are however, that this approach is based on a number of assumptions. One being that the data is available and correct, that the current provision is targeted against agreed organisational standards and that these targets are correct. In addition this process does not collect data which is less precise. For example it is possible to identify the number of staff who currently hold diplomas, however it would not be possible, without further definition to identify those who are at diploma level.

Overall however this systematic macro approach, linked to effective databases can be very useful for planning purposes.

A combination of approaches

To overcome the potential disadvantages inherent in various approaches it is often most effective to utilise a combination of methods.

For example the authors have utilised the following combinations in previous TNAs:

- questionnaire and interviews
- questionnaire and focus groups (Ward, 1993)
- marginal analysis and focus groups
- marginal analysis and interviews (Ward, 1997).

One approach can be utilised as a preliminary step to the other. For example the results of questionnaires can help formulate interview schedules and vice-versa.

No one combination can be considered the best. Choice is dependant on the objectives of the TNA, the size of the population, the culture of the organisation and the resources available.

Individual performance review systems (IPR)

As stated earlier IPR is one approach to measuring performance and identifying the development needs of individuals.This section focuses on the organisation's role in introducing the IPR process, an example of the process itself and a discussion of what can go wrong, and how to potentially overcome this.

At the organisational level there is a need to ensure that effective systems are in place. This entails ensuring that the overall process is agreed, that managers have appropriate preparation, and that all individuals understand the underlying principles.

Figure 4.4 shows an example of the process (Taken from Armstrong, 1991 with permission).

Figure 4.4: performance measurement

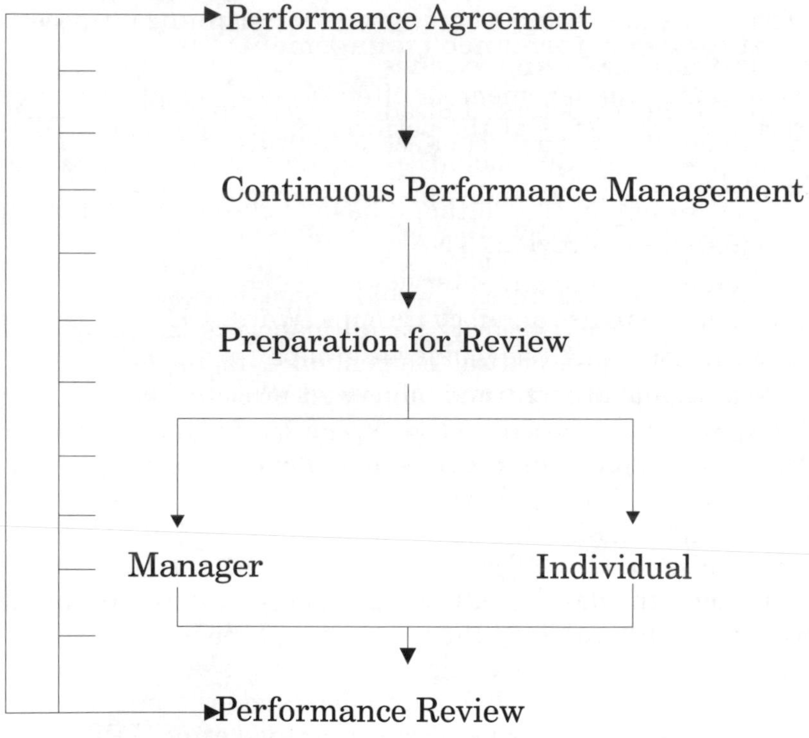

The performance agreement

It is important to ensure that performance is measured against agreed expectations. As stated earlier, this may be in the form of competencies or standards, relating to the performance process or be outcome based in the form of objectives. The latter, also known as management by objectives (MBO), is commonly utilised to measure manager's performance. As with the earlier discussion relating to objectives in strategy formulation, it is essential that there is a clear understanding of what is to be achieved, when this needs to be done by and who is responsible for what elements.

MBO may not be appropriate for all staff groups, and it may be more useful to utilise competencies or a combined approach with MBO, for example performance may initially be measured against competencies, with appropriate objectives then identified to be achieved over a particular time period.

Continuous performance management

Performance management is often seen as being a one-off process which occurs at the performance review stage. To be effective however, this should be ongoing with established time set aside to discuss an individual's performance, give feedback opportunities and to identify any further development needs. In reality this is often said to be difficult in healthcare mainly due to time constraints. I would argue however that this process should be a priority for all managers, as managing people is the most critical element of a manager's role. If utilised, this approach is dynamic and proactive rather than reactive. That is, time can be saved by having a planned approach, rather than constantly having to respond to problems.

Preparation for review

In respect of the formal review process, preparation is essential. This is both by the manager and the individual. The manager needs to ensure that not only are the time and place agreed, but that the individual understands the purpose and how they are expected to prepare.

Both should then take time to prepare by considering the following:

- have competencies and/or set objectives been achieved?
- what has been the overall performance during the review period?
- what are the individual's strengths and weaknesses?

- have skills been utilised?
- are there any perceived development needs?
- what are the potential future objectives?

This should then be recorded in note format for utilisation at the performance review interview. An example of preparation forms for both managers and individuals are included in *Appendices VIII* and *IX*.

Performance review

The actual review should then consist of a discussion of the preparatory notes. Initially concentrate on past and current performance, with the latter stages dedicated to the identification of future objectives, development needs and opportunities. There should be no shocks at this stage if performance has been managed on an ongoing basis.

It is vital that any objectives and/or opportunities which are defined, are understandable, measurable, realistic and achievable.

Each individual should also have a clear understanding as to who is responsible for what. For example, if a development need has been noted, who is responsible for identifying appropriate opportunities — the manager or the individual?

The interview should then be recorded in a format that suits the organisation. An example is shown in *Appendix X*.

It is useful to also involve the manager's manager in reviewing the recorded outcome. This is for a number of reasons which include:

- it enables the manager's performance to be reviewed
- it helps to eliminate any potential individual personality conflicts affecting the process
- it is also part of the feedback process; information can then be utilised in departmental training and development plans.

Potential problems with IPR process

There are a number of problems that can occur with IPR. Managers need to be aware of these in order to help prevent their occurrence. These include:

- Lack of perceived organisational commitment. IPR must be seen to apply at all levels. Commitment must also be shown in terms of time and effort devoted to the process, and to ensuring that managers have the knowledge base and skills to undertake IPR. Managers must also be held to account for the implementation of IPR.
- Performance review systems often fail due to a lack of understanding, and the apparent values and beliefs in the organisation. For example if IPR is seen as punitive, then it is difficult to convince people of its role in individual and organisational development.
- As stated in *Chapter 2*, conflict can occur in the process itself, particularly if linked to performance related pay (PRP). As stated previously Bevan and Thompson (1991) state this may happen, because in order to demonstrate a need, the individual may feel that they are acknowledging a weakness. Kinnie and Lowe (1990) state that this is the classic 'coach/judge' dilemma that managers face in managing performance.
- In order to work there must be explicit standards/ objectives against which the individual can be measured (Shepherd, 1993). These may not always be realistic, measurable or perceived as owned by the individual.
- If the individual and manager's responsibilities for taking action post review are not clearly defined, the process may break down. This also occurs if there is no follow-up, and if this is perceived as an annual event only.
- The framework/systems may not appropriately meet the organisational needs. Although this can sometimes occur, in the author's experience, elements of the framework eg. the paperwork are often blamed for ineffective review processes, when other causes exist; eg. manager's lack of understanding, or a disbelief in the benefits of the process itself.

How to overcome potential problems

There are a number of steps that can be taken. These include:

- demonstrable management commitment, in the form of launching any new systems; commitment of resource; accountability for action and the process occurring at all levels
- ensure that the underlying principles are understood, not only by managers but individual practitioners
- ensure managers have the required knowledge base, attitudes and skills to undertake the process
- ongoing evaluation
- ensure the process is not just an annual review process, but that it is part of the organisational performance management system, with feedback mechanisms into departmental and organisational planning processes.

Conclusion

This chapter has highlighted a number of pragmatic approaches to how training and development needs can be identified from the organisational perspective. This concludes issues relating to macro approaches.

The following chapters will now concentrate on the same issues from the individual practitioner's perspective — the micro perspective.

References

Armstrong M (1991) *A Handbook of Personnel Management Practice* 4th ed. Kogan Page, London

Bashford P (1991) How to identify training needs. *Nurs Times* **87**:57

Beaumont G (1996) *A review of 100 NVQs/SVQs (The Beaumont report)* Evaluation Advisory Group. Department for Education and Employment, London

Bevan S, Thompson M (1991) Performance management at the crossroads. *Personnel Management* Nov 1991

Kinnie N, Lowe D (1990) Performance related pay on the shopfloor *Personnel Management* Nov 1990

McClelland SB (1994a) Training needs assessment data gathering methods, part 1, survey questionnaires. *Journal of European Industrial Training* **18**(1): 22–6

McClelland SB (1994b) Training needs assessment data gathering methods, part 2, individual interviews. *Journal of European Industrial Training* **18**(2):94

McClelland SB (1994c) Training needs assessment data gathering methods, part 3 focus groups. *Journal of European Industrial Training* **18**(3):29–32

Oppenheim AN (1966) *Questionnaire Design And Attitude Measurement.* Heinemann, London.

Ritchie J, Spencer L (1994) Qualitative data analysis for applied policy research. In: Bryman A, Burgess RG (1994) *Analysing Qualitative Data.* Routledge, London

Shepherd JC (1993) *Training Needs Analysis of Qualified Nurse Practitioners Across Three Health Authorities.* Unpublished PhD Thesis. University of Birmingham

Teasdale K (1992) Training needs analysis overview *Health Services Management* **88**(7): 23

Ward C (1993) Overcoming potential dissonance between organisational and individual development needs. In: Management development and the changing role of the ward manager. *J Nurs Management.* Supplement 1 Vol 1.

Ward C (1997) *An Exploration Of Macro v Micro Approaches to Identifying the Training and Development Needs of Qualified Nursing Staff.* Unpublished MBA Thesis. University of Warwick

Youngman MR (1986) *Analysing Questionnaires.* University of Nottingham School of Education, Nottingham

5

Micro approaches: political, professional and personal factors affecting individual development

This chapter will review the governmental, political and professional policies that affect the nurse, midwife and health visitor in continuing in their chosen field of practice.

Self development: what are the drivers and forces?

The first step in career development begins as the individual chooses and undertakes their initial training programme. It is at this stage that the career starts to focus on to a particular area of care, ie. adult, mental health, midwifery, mental illness or children's nursing. Each training programme provides the individual with unique experiences and knowledge that affects the practitioner throughout their career. These experiences then influence, and somewhat dictate how the individual can progress within their chosen field of practice, providing opportunities and yet constraints for their areas of practice.

In healthcare the individual practitioner is required to continue to develop and gain new knowledge in order to maintain and improve their care as their world consistently changes. Burnard (1989) notes that what the individual learns at one stage in their career cannot hold throughout their career. Practice can quickly become dated and even dangerous if new practices, technology and research are not developed and incorporated in to the care given. Grant (1992) notes that only half of professional competence developed from a taught programme is learned therefore half of the course becomes obsolete on completion of that programme.

The forces and drivers that challenge and constrain the individual to develop their career and practice come from a variety of sources both within and outside their area of practice. These forces and drivers include governmental policies, professional requirements, employers needs, educational opportunities and internal goals from the practitioner themselves. Each force/driver has its own agenda that demands a given direction and development required of the individual practitioner. It is important for the practitioner that when identifying and planning their career they acknowledge these drivers and forces, as they may have direct affect on their chosen pathway.

Each driver/force will be addressed in relation to its own perceived agenda.

Governmental policies

As the internal market has gained momentum over the past years, governmental policies have been introduced which directly influence the individual practitioner in their practice and performance. These policies require the individual to maintain and develop their practice within given settings. The emphasis for most of these policies is on improving the quality of care for the patient/client.

There are several governmental policies that directly affect the practitioners and how they develop their level of competence and performance. These policies are mandatory for all those registered practitioners working within the healthcare arena. These policies include: *The Patient's Charter* (DoH, 1991); *Health of the Nation* (DoH, 1992); *Our Healthier Nation* (DoH, 1998); *Vision for the Future* (DoH, 1993); *Heathrow Debate* (DoH, 1993); *Greehalgh Report* (DoH, 1994) and the *NHS Executive Priorities and Planning Guidance* (DoH, 1995).

The Patient's Charter (DoH, 1991)

The Patient's Charter (DoH, 1991) set out to identify what the consumers of healthcare can expect from the providers of care. It established nine national charter standards which are aimed specifically at the quality of care provided. One of these standards states that:

> *..a named qualified nurse, midwife or health visitor for each patient responsible for their nursing and midwifery care*

Qualified practitioners have always been accountable and responsible for the care they administer under the Nurse, Midwives and Health Visitors Act (DHSS, 1979). *The Patient's Charters* emphasis is on an individual registered practitioner being named, who holds accountability for the client's care whilst they are a customer of that service.

The charter also provides the opportunity for practitioners to influence the way nursing and midwifery care is given and an opportunity to shape the way these services are provided in the future.

The practitioner can no longer rely on old knowledge learnt in their basic training as this practice may be out dated and even lead to dangerous practice in a changing environment. If the practitioners are to take responsibility for the care they give, taking the lead in patient care, then they must maintain and develop their clinical competence in their chosen field of practice, in order to be accountable for the practice performed.

Local policies have also been developed from the charter and as consumers become more familiar with these, demand increases for the practitioner to have a greater understanding of the care they are providing. The nurse, health visitor or midwife takes on the role of becoming a resource of information for the client/patient, an advocate for the patient's and carer's needs, and ultimately holds the accountability for their client's/patient's care.

The individual in this situation cannot separate themselves from this policy, and therefore the notion of accountability and responsibility requires the individual to develop their practice. This is not therefore dependant on whether or not they wish to progress to a higher status in order to deliver a knowledgeable, empowering patient centred service.

Health of the Nation (DoH, 1992)

The aim of this governmental paper was to provide a strategy to improve the general health of the population by increasing life expectancy and preventing premature death. Issues for the healthcare professional here identify their involvement in how the standards of good practice and clinical protocols were to be moved forward. The paper identifies the commitment of the professionals as vital in the achieving of these objectives. The practitioner again is faced with playing a vital part in the achieving of this policy and needs to develop skills in health promotion, screening programmes, dealing with stress and helping the bereaved families, giving of advice and forming alliances with other healthcare professionals and colleagues. Often these skills are absent in pre registration programmes and developed on an ad hoc basis through practice and experience.

The paper states that it requires:

> *health professionals individually and in alliance with others to share knowledge and empower their clients to make decisions, altering lifestyle and improve the quality of life.*

To empower consumers and achieve these goals the individual practitioner will be required to gain sufficient knowledge in clinical and cognitive knowledge bases which affect their practice. Again as the profession enters into more research and evidence based practice, it is the individual's responsibility to develop their personal knowledge base in order to empower their client/patient. To work with other colleagues also requires the practitioner to develop leadership skills, negotiation skills and often a higher level of cognitive skill to collaborate with other allied medical staff and be a valued member of the professional team. To share that knowledge demands some educational skills in the dissemination of knowledge to others. These skills are often developed after the pre registration training, formalisation of this learning is then the practitioner's responsibility.

With the change in government the production of the paper *Our Healthier Nation* (DoH, 1998) continues to address these issues.

Vision for the Future (DoH, 1993)

The *Vision for the Future* (DoH, 1993) document draws on the 'Strategy for Nursing' (1989a) where the emphasis was on developing practice, manpower, education, leadership and management. It stresses the importance of a flexible, knowledgeable, and skilful response to the needs of users of the service. The document targets five specific areas these include:

- quality and audit
- accountability for practice
- clinical and professional leadership
- clinical research and supervision
- purchasing and commissioning.

The credible clinical professional practitioner is again identified in relation to providing a high quality of care. Through this process the department will continue to identify good practise and evaluate progress. As practitioners continue to practise, their expertise will be brought into question if they fail as an individual to demonstrate competence in their chosen area of practice under this policy.

Accountability in a changing environment brings its own demands as individuals strive not only to keep pace with the developing technology, but also the growing pool of research leading to changes within clinical practice.

Clinical supervision and professional leadership have also been identified as key areas within the *Vision for the Future* (DoH, 1993) document. These incorporate the importance of valuing and enhancing the individual's practice. As NHS Trusts and organisations implement the process of clinical supervision into their strategies and it is embraced by the practitioners it can provide the opportunity for individual's to identify their own needs in relation to personal, experiential and scientific knowledge bases. Clinical supervision provides a safe environment allowing the individual to reflect on their practice and develop their own knowledge through the guidance of an experienced practitioner (Johns, 1995). The practitioner can use this process to gain guidance from significant others in their field of practice in relation to their future career pathway.

Heathrow Debate (DoH, 1993)

The *Heathrow Debate* (1993) discussed the challenges for nurses and midwifery in the 21st century and identified eight strategic issues:

- contribution of nursing to the individual
- context of nursing
- team work
- substitution
- education and training
- authority, responsibility, accountability
- regulation
- public perception of nursing.

The debate noted that health promotion, health education and screening should have a high profile in the work that nurses do. There is a potential gap between the practitioner's level of knowledge that was gained during their pre registration training and the demands of this paper in relation to some individual's field of practice. These specific areas of practice may demand continuing educational needs for the individual to be equipped to deal with new and changing areas of practice.

The roles of healthcare providers is changing with the shift of care into the community, following the *NHS and Community Care Act* (1990). This has provided more scope for independent and self employed nurses working within a range of coalitions with other professionals. For this process of change to occur the individual practitioner requires further training and experience in the care of clients within the client's/patient's home environment.

The *Heathrow Debate* (DoH, 1993) noted the role of education and training for practitioners as they strive to gain these new skills and knowledge in practice and for some to gain further qualifications.

Greenhalgh Report (DoH, 1994)

The Greenhalgh Report (1994) commissioning body was set up to review the interface between junior doctors and nurses. The Department of Health commissioned this group to improve the living and working conditions, clinical experiences and training of junior doctors. The main aim of the study was:

> *to contribute to the improvement in patient care by examining the interface between junior hospital doctors and ward nurses, with a view to enhancing the role of nurses and reducing the inappropriate workload of the junior hospital doctor.*

This report has initiated much debate in the nursing literature, as the attempt to define 'inappropriate workload' is highlighted as a contentious issue. The report states that there have been certain activities that have been performed by junior doctors that can be suitably performed by trained nurses. In order for the performance of some of these tasks there is an implication that further development and training of new skills and knowledge needs to be given to gain competence and safe practice in the expanded practice role. The implications are for both formal and informal education and training programmes. The programmes are often related to skills such as IV therapy, blood sampling and advanced life support. Each course is competency based and often relates to the performance of the psychomotor skill rather than the development of new knowledge. As the report has taken on momentum the professional bodies have debated the role of the nurse and recently the United Kingdom Central Council (UKCC, 1990) have introduced the concept of the specialist and advanced practitioner. Although there is much debate and confusion over these roles (Castledine, 1995; UKCC, 1996; Rolf and Philips, 1997) the potential for practitioners to move nursing practice forward have been made available. These roles to date, as stated earlier, often have been associated with a higher level of education such as Degree and Masters level study. These initiatives will have a direct effect on the career choice of the practitioner who wishes to proceed down the route of specialism or advanced practice.

NHS Executive Priorities and Planning Guidance for NHS 1996/97 (NHSE, 1995)

This document states that there is a need to:

> *Develop NHS organisations as good employers with particular reference to workforce planning, education and training, employment policy and practice and the development of team work, reward systems, staff utilisation and staff welfare.*

Although here the emphasis is on the employer, the development for the individual practitioner is implicit, if they are to provide a quality service to the purchasers of care. Again the concept and opportunity for education and training offers the individual the opportunity to review areas of further study.

Professional requirements

There have been a number of reports and policy documents from the professional bodies that provides both the opportunity and the responsibility for the individual practitioner to develop their practice and clinical expertise. These requirements include the Post Registration Education and Practice Project (PREP)(UKCC, 1990), Professional Code of Conduct (UKCC, 1992), Standards for Education and Practice following Registration (UKCC, 1994a) and the Creating Lifelong Learners Partnerships for Care (ENB, 1994a).

Each report identifies mandatory requirements for future individual development and provides opportunities for practitioners to maintain and develop their clinical expertise both through their practice or through the provision of educational opportunities.

Post Registration Education and Practice (UKCC, 1990)

In an effort ensure a higher quality of care, to further develop and to ensure professional standards are maintained and developed the United Kingdom Central Council for Nurses

Midwives and Health Visitors issued the Post Registration Education and Practice Project Report (1990).

This report provided the opportunity for each practitioner to contribute to the debate of future development of practitioners. The document states that:

> *During the three years leading up to periodic registration, all nurses must provide evidence of appropriate professional learning by completing a minimum of five days study leave.*

The document also initially discussed the notion of the specialist and advanced practitioner level and has brought a growing expectation amongst qualified practitioners that they should strive towards gaining a higher level of academic study in order to maintain their registration. This is not the case; although there is opportunity for study, the main aim of the report is to provide the individual with the opportunity to develop and maintain their clinical skills and competence through practice. Although the document identifies a period of five study days it includes 'or appropriate professional learning'. The practitioner does not therefore have to strive to attend courses or gain higher qualifications, but must demonstrate that they have developed and maintained their clinical competence in practice. This may include formal learning, reviewing literature, attending teaching sessions or through experiential learning and reflection.

It is an opportunity for the practitioner to learn from their own practice, and identify any areas or gaps in their knowledge base. The requirements of this report are that the individual practitioner identifies and records where their practice has developed. The introduction of the PREP document does however affect the chosen pathway for the individual, as these requirements must be taken into consideration when planning for future development. Development must be relevant to the individual's area of practice.

Professional code of conduct

The Professional Code of Conduct (UKCC, 1992) has provided nurses, health visitors and midwives with an accountability clause. It states that:

> *Practitioners must endeavour always to achieve, maintain and develop knowledge, skills and competence to respond to those needs and interests*

The professional code was developed as a result of the Nurses, Health Visitors and Midwives Act (1979) and charges the individual practitioner with the accountability clause. Again it identifies the need for practitioners to develop and maintain their practice in order to safeguard their client/patient. As medical care becomes used to the world of litigation, alongside increasing use of technology and changing practice through improved research skills, it is in the practitioner's interest to continually update that practice, maintaining competence. The Midwives Code of Practice (UKCC, 1994b) also sets out similar standards and requirements.

Standards for education and practice following registration (1994)

The United Kingdom Central Council in this document stated that:

> *The continuing demands and complexity of professional practice requires registered practitioners to not only maintain and develop their professional knowledge and competence, but to do so in the interests of patient and client care.*

This document again identifies the notion of the practitioner continually developing their individual knowledge and competence. The emphasis is again to safeguard the client/patient and notes the complexity of the healthcare environment. As with governmental policies the client/patient is the focus of that development and emphasis is on increased quality of service provision.

Creating lifelong learners, partnerships for care English National Board (ENB, 1994)

Although this document produced by the ENB focuses on the educational opportunities for the individual practitioner, it notes that healthcare professionals should be encouraged to become continual learners throughout their career and not to rely on their initial training. It notes the value of educational programmes introducing procedures to develop an enquiring professional who will continue to seek knowledge throughout their career.

The ENB is also concerned with the educational opportunities for healthcare professionals and provides a quality audit in the production of professionally based courses. Opportunities are provided for the individual who wishes to gain further qualifications in a given speciality, or other appropriate professional learning.

With the moving of the education of nursing into universities and colleges of higher education, more courses have become available for the practitioner to move to higher levels of academic study. Much debate surrounds the notion of an all graduate profession and this may affect some individuals as they plan for a longer career in healthcare.

Employer/organisational drivers

Although these have been identified from the employer perspective in *Chapter 4* they will still have a major impact on the individuals choice of career development. In this new market environment where 'value for money' drives the quality assurance process, Duffield *et al* (1996) notes that this climate may distract the focus on quality by the individual practitioner.

In past years a great deal of time and finance has been given to the development of introducing quality, audit and standard setting however as Harvey and Kitson (1996) note there is limited evidence to date suggesting that these systems are having any significant impact in terms of changing practice and ultimately improving quality of nursing care. As Trusts and employers seek to adopt and maintain further initiatives such as Investors in People standards, the goals for individual development may be dictated by their employer to fit organisational strategies and goals.

Educational drivers

Traditionally education has been regarded as an end in itself (Dewey, 1916). As well as the changing and demanding role that the practitioner finds themselves in, the role of education has also had to undergo major reviews. The emphasis now is on the learning rather than on the teaching and the emergence of the 'knowledgeable doer' with the introduction of *Project 2000* (UKCC, 1987) and lifelong learner concept (ENB, 1994).

In 1989 the Department of Health issued a white paper *Working for Patients* (DoH, 1989b). Paper number 10 in this series addressed the issue of financial support for the pre registration and recordable qualifications. As nursing, midwifery and health visiting preparation has now moved into universities and colleges of higher education the employers have developed consortia to contract for educational places (Bamford, 1997). Based on the employer's strategy and training needs analysis the consortia contract the money for these courses with the relevant educational institution. This has a direct affect on the individual who wishes to apply for funding for further academic qualifications. The employer will contract a number of places for an identified programme. This may or may not suit the needs of the individual and therefore consideration should be taken of all parts by the employer and individual before embarking on the courses so that the appropriate individual receives the funding.

As discussed earlier, the emergence of the nurse practitioner, specialist and advanced practitioner has raised some further opportunities relating to educational requirements. An identified level of practice has been, and continues to be discussed within the profession in relation to the specialist and advanced practitioner. The advanced practitioner however is currently recognised in most areas as those practitioners who are at a post graduate academic level qualification (Dunn, 1997) while the specialist practitioner currently remains at degree level (English National Board, 1994). Much debate continues in the literature as to the level of competence for these individuals and at what level this practitioner should be performing at in their practice (Lillyman, 1998).

With the move into higher education, degrees for nurses, midwives and health visitors are offered in a variety of subjects from the English National Board Higher Award. This is the qualification given at degree level in relation to identified characteristics that the individual has to achieve within their practice, to that of specialist practitioner award as described within the UKCC Post Registration and Education documents (UKCC, 1990). Degrees in nursing or allied healthcare are also offered as post registration courses and can improve the choices for practitioners who wish to expand their knowledge in relation to issues such as health promotion, health studies, management, teaching etc. With all these options now available the choice becomes more confusing to the practitioner. They need to decide at what academic level they wish to pursue their studies and then in what subject or speciality does that study need to be addressed in order to gain the relevant qualification for their future career. Guidance is important for the practitioner in this area and can often be obtained from a career guidance structure within the educational establishment.

Individual motivation

Having discussed the external forces and driver that may affect the individual practitioner when reviewing their professional and academic choices in the chosen pathway, we must not forget the individual who possesses their own drivers that force them on to higher levels within the organisation. These drivers may come from the financial rewards offered within the posts available, the prestige in gaining higher levels of practice or the drive for self actualisation in their role and increasing confidence in themselves.

Hyde and Wright (1997) suggest that responsibility for ones own development engenders awareness and responsibility on the part of the individual. Many individuals in striving to keep up with the demands from the other drivers stated above may also notice gaps in their own knowledge base and strive through personal learning, research and personal development to fill those gaps without formal education or support from employers.

Conclusion

Each of the governmental and professional polices discussed identified several key areas for the individual practitioner to consider when planning their careers. These include:

- quality care
- competence in practice
- education and training
- accountability.

As stated the practitioner can no longer rest on their initial qualification gained at registration if they are to meet the governmental and professional requirements in the ever changing and challenging healthcare arena. With increased accountability for practice and the striving for a good quality service, the onus for development is on the individual's contributions for the organisation in which they work.

These documents must be taken into consideration by the practitioner when planning their future. The mandatory considerations by all the documents stated is that the practitioner strives to maintain and develop their clinical competence in order to provide a safe environment for their client/patient. Any further or higher forms of formal education are up to the individual concerned and not a direct requirement from the government or professional bodies. However in choosing an educational pathway the practitioner must be aware of these developments and observe the debates surrounding the specialist and advanced practitioner.

References

Bamford M (1997) Funding issues in education and training. In: Morton Cooper A, Bamford M (1997) *Excellence in healthcare Management*. Blackwell Science, London

Burnard P (1989) Developing critical ability in nurse education. *Nurse Education Today* **9**: 271–5

Castledine G (1995) Defining specialist practice. *Brit J Nurs* **4**(5): 264–5

Department of Health (1979) *Nurses, Midwives and Health Visitors Act*. HMSO, London

Department of Health (1989a) *A Strategy for Nursing: Report of the Steering Committee*. HMSO, London

Department of Health (1989b) *Working for Patients*. HMSO, London

Department of Health (1990) *NHS and Community Care Act*. HMSO, London

Department of Health (1991) *The Patients' Charter*. HMSO, London

Department of Health (1992) *Health of the Nation: A Strategy for Health in England*. HMSO, London

Department of Health (1993) *Vision For The Future. The Nursing, Midwifery and Health Visitors Contribution to Health and healthcare*. HMSO, London

Department of Health (1993) *The Challenges For Nursing And Midwifery In The 21st Century. A Report of the Heathrow Debate*. HMSO, London

Department of Health (1995) *NHS Executive Priorities and Planning Guidance*. HMSO, London

Department of Health (1998) *Our Healthier Nation*. HMSO, London

Dewey J (1916) *Democracy and Education*. Free Press, New York In: Jarvis P (1992) Quality in practice the role of education. *Nurse Education Today* **12:** 3–10

Duffield C, Donoghue J, Pelletier D (1996) Do clinical nurse specialists and nursing unit managers believe the provision of quality care is important. *J Adv Nurs* **24:** 334–40

Dunn L (1997) A literature review of advanced nursing practice in the USA. *J Adv Nurs* **25**: 814–19

English National Board for Nurses, Midwives and Health Visitors (1994) *Creating Life Long Learners Partnerships for Care*. ENB, London

Grant R (1992) Obsolescence or lifelong education: choices and challenges. *Physiotherapy* **78**(3): 167–71

Greenhalgh and Co (1994) *The Interface Between Junior Doctors and Nurses: A Research Study for the Department of Health Executive Summary*. Greenhalgh and Co, Macclesfield

Harvey G, Kitson A (1996) Achieving improvement through quality: an evaluation of key factors in the implementation process. *J Adv Nurs* 24: 185–95

Hyde J, Wright A (1997) Self development. *Nursing Management* **4**(3): 10–11

Johns C (1995) The value of reflective practice for nursing. *Journal of Clinical Nursing* **4**: 23–30

Lillyman S (1998) Assessing competence in Mcgee and Castledine specialist and advanced practitioners. Blackwell Science, London (in press)

NHSE (1995) *Priorities and Planning Guidance for the NHS 1996/97*. DoH, London

Rolfe G, Phillips LM (1997) The development and evaluation of the role of an advanced practitioner in dementia: an action research project. *International Nursing Studies* **34**(2): 119–27

United Kingdom Central Council (1987) *Project Paper 9 Project 2000: The Final Proposals*. UKCC, London

United Kingdom Central Council (1990) *Post Registration Education and Practice Project*. UKCC, London

United Kingdom Central Council (1992) *Code of Professional Conduct for the Nurse, Midwife and Health Visitor* 3rd ed. UKCC, London

United Kingdom Central Council (1992) *The Scope of Professional Practice*. UKCC, London

United Kingdom Central Council (1994a) *Standards for Education and Practice Following Registration*. UKCC, London

United Kingdom Central Council (1994b) *Midwives Code of Practice*. UKCC, London

United Kingdom Central Council (1996) *Registrars Letter on the Complexities Involved in Distinguishing the terms NP/ANP/SNP*. UKCC, London

6

Methods, strategies and tools for individual development

The previous chapter has identified 'why' individual practitioners are required, by governmental, professional and organisational bodies, to develop and improve their professional competence and practice.

This chapter will seek to identify 'how' some of the methods and systems currently employed within the healthcare arena may assist the individual in planing their own developmental and career structure.

As Hyde and Wright (1997) noted the lack of any systematic organisational approach to development can lead to an anarchic environment where the individual is vying with their peers in order to gain the best advantage. This does not assist the individual or organisation achieve their goals. The business agenda, as noted by Young (1996), is now seen as a key activity for both managers and professionals and it has wide ranging repercussions for the way individuals carry out their work and plan their future career. Each of the approaches discussed below will be examined from the individual perspective of development needs. This chapter will assist the individual in the identification and planning of their individual programme of development in order to maintain and develop their competence in practice in line with the Professional Code of Conduct (UKCC, 1992) and PREP (UKCC, 1990).

Many organisations currently employ strategies for individual development with the opportunity to meet and contribute to the wider business of the organisation. These approaches include individual performance review, staff appraisal systems, peer review, self development strategies and clinical supervision. These approaches will be reviewed in the light of the individual planning their career. External agencies that incorporate development strategies will also be addressed.

Staff appraisals

In respect of the above the National Staff Committee (Nurses and Midwives) stated in 1977 that:

> *The prime objective of the revised scheme is to improve performance with the ultimate aim of improving the effectiveness of the nursing service. To this end the role of appraisal is seen by the committee to be:*
>
> *a) to increase the contribution of individual nurses in their current job and*
>
> *b) to develop their potential abilities to meet the needs of the service of the future.*

Staff appraisal as identified by Walton (1988) is not an opportunity for the manager to reprimand or present a list of 'this year's faults' to the practitioner. The process should not be one sided, but involve an honest open discussion. The aim of staff appraisal is to discuss together the total situation in relation to the individual's performance. Its particular focus is to make constructive use of experience and think about subsequent action and performance to improve and develop practice. The appraisal also provides opportunity for the manager to talk about how they have also affected the individual's practice and the clinical environment in which they work.

The appraisal process aims to provide both the manager and practitioner with an agreed action plan that addresses individual development for the following year.

The individual should take the opportunity prior to this meeting to reflect on their current knowledge base and skills relating to their current area of work and how they as an individual can contribute to the organisational goals. This appraisal consists of an annual meeting with the direct line manager.

Individual performance review

Individual performance review is a process that has been introduced within the NHS over the last few decades. It is a process that originated within the business world and has been devolved to the clinical arena.

Individual performance review (IPR) consists of two broad aims; it is a tool for managers to implement departmental/unit needs and wider organisational strategies and secondly for the individual to identify their own development needs and objectives. The review is usually carried out annually with a six monthly review.

The process consists of a manager and practitioner identifying the strategy/plan/priority statement of the organisation, individual unit or department. It will attempt to review how the individual can assist in the achievement of these goals and the individual's objectives and goals are set for the following year. As with appraisal it involves both parties agreeing individual objectives and goals, however, IPR is more individually focused with the practitioner identifying their objective in line with the organisational needs at differing levels of practice. The process begins with the manager's IPR, followed by a series of top down IPR's. This strategy helps to identify the continuance of objectives down through each level.

The outcome of the IPR involves an agreed set of objectives. The IPR process is discussed in more detail in *Chapter 4*.

Peer review

In line with staff appraisal and IPR, some organisations include a peer review system. This potentially has problems in the area of staff development as the peer may not be in a position to provide further advice on available procedures and opportunities available within the organisation. The system will provide the opportunity to reflect on the current status for the individual and may provide another perspective from their peers. This system of peer review can work well with the mentor/preceptor approach where a colleague of the same grade is responsible for the supervision and development of the student or newly qualified member of staff. The role involves identifying immediate learning needs and development for the individual while working or settling into the clinical area. Although this is a form of peer review the individual providing the advice should be a more experienced practitioner who is able to support and disseminate knowledge and skills to their 'mentee' or 'preceptee'.

There have been potential disadvantages to this approach as there has always been the informal system where the individuals share their experiences over a coffee break. This situation often involves reflection on the negative aspects of the role rather than positive points and does not necessarily provide a structured approach to development.

Self development strategies

Where formal systems are not in operation individuals cannot afford to neglect their professional development. Personal development as noted in *Chapter 5* is a requirement of governmental policies and professional guidelines (UKCC, 1995).

As individuals take on the role of professional development and the development of their clinical competence, there has been an associated move towards reflective practice. This is an active process described by Schon (1983) as where the individual reflects 'in' or 'on' their practice. This reflection then forms the basis for analysis of the action taken in the given situation and provides the individual with the opportunity to gain further insight, develop new knowledge or justify their practice. A model of reflection can therefore be utilised to assist the individual with their development plan. Ghaye and Lillyman (1997) identify a number of models of reflection.

Clinical supervision

It was the publication of the document *A Vision for the Future* (DoH, 1993) which identified clinical supervision as being at the top of the professional agenda. This has since become an issue which has widely been discussed within the healthcare arena. The 'vision' consists of five key areas: quality of care; outcomes and audit; accountability for practice; clinical and professional leadership; research and supervision; purchasing and commissioning and education and practice (Fowler, 1996). Barber and Norman (1987) note four main functions of supervision, these include education, management, support and the development of self awareness.

Butterworth and Faugier (1992) state that clinical supervision is an exchange between practising professionals to enable the development of professional skills. The Department of Health in their document *A Vision for the Future* (1993) stated that clinical supervision was:

> *a term used to describe a formal process of professional support and learning which enables practitioners to develop knowledge and competence, assume responsibility for their own practice and enhance consumer protection and safety of care in complex clinical situations. It is central to the process of learning and the expansion of the scope of practice and should be seen as a means of encouraging self assessment and analytical and reflective skills*

Fish and Twin (1997) note that clinical supervision involves gaining an insight into practice by means of investigating, reflecting, theorising, challenging, and considering its moral significance and implications in order to improve future practice.

This process, as described by Proctor (1986), involves a second individual either manger, peer or group of individuals who can assist the individual in identifying the process of reflecting on their practice. It is in this situation, as in reflective practice, that the individual can identify gaps in their current knowledge and gain relevant knowledge and skills through further study or experiential learning within their practice. The supervisor provides a different perspective and allows the individual to gain insight and to recognise any gaps in their knowledge and skill. Unlike IPR and staff appraisal clinical supervision does not reflect the organisational goals, but offers the opportunity for the practitioner to reflect on and learn from their experience.

External organisations

Many of the professional unions offer external support and guidance to the individual practitioner in their choice of career pathway. The Royal college of Nursing in 1995 produced, as part of their Nurses in Leadership Project 'A guide to planning your career' (RCN, 1995). They also provide a phone in service for their members, 'nurseline', that offers confidential advice on the development of their individual career.

Summary

Individuals may have one or more of these approaches within their clinical area. To gain full use of them they need to be aware of the overall organisation goals and the unit/department's strategy in order to identify where they fit in as individuals and how they can with their own development assist in the overall plan. All approaches include reflection on their past achievements and a negotiated and agreed action plan for their future developments.

References

Barber P, Norman I (1987) Skills in supervision. *Nurs Times* **1**(87): 56–7

Butterworth J, Faugier J (1992) *Clinical Supervision and Mentorship in Nursing*. Chapman Hall, London

Department of Health (1993) *A Vision for the Future. The Nursing Midwifery and Health Visitor Contribution to Health and Healthcare.* HMSO, London

Fish D, Twin S (1997) *Quality Clinical Supervision in the healthcare Professionals.* Butterworth and Heinemann, London

Fowler J (1996) The organisation of clinical supervision within the nursing profession: a review of the literature. *J Adv Nurs* **23**: 471–8

Ghaye T, Lillyman S (1997) *Learning Journals and Critical Incidents: Reflective Practice for the Healthcare Professionals.* Quay Books Mark Allen Publishing, Dinton

Hawkins P, Shohet R (1989) *Getting the Support and Supervision You Need. Supervision in the Helping Professions.* Open University Press, Milton Keynes

Hyde J, Wright A (1997) Self development nursing management *Nursing Management* **4**(3): 10–11

National Staff Committee (Nurses and Midwives) (1977) *NHS Staff Development and Performance Review - Nurses, Midwives, Health visitors and Tutorial Staff.* DHSS, London

Proctor S (1986) Supervision: a co operative exercise in accountability. In: Marken P, Payne M eds. (1986) *Enabling and Ensuring.* Leicester National Youth Bureau and Council for Education and Training in Youth Work and Community Work, Leicester

Royal College of Nursing (1995) *A Guide to Planning Your Career.* RCN, London

Schon, D (1983) *The Reflective Practitioner: How Professionals Think in Action.* Basic Books, New York

United Kingdom Central Council (1990) *Post Registration Education and Practice.* UKCC, London

United Kingdom Central Council (1992) *Professional Code of Conduct for Nurses, Midwives and Health Visitors.* UKCC, London

United Kingdom Central Council (1995) *Standards for Post Registration Education and Practice.* UKCC, London

Walton M (1988) *Management and Managing, A Dynamic Approach.* Harper and Row, London

Young A (1996) Who sets the business agenda? *J Nurs Management* **4:** 347–52

7

Career profiling for the individual and organisation

This chapter focuses upon career profile, for the individual and organisation to use when developing an action plan for individual development. It draws on all the macro and micro drivers and forces discussed in the previous chapters and identifies a way forward for future development.

The career profile has been adapted from the Institute of Personnel and Development (1995) and provides a framework for the nurse, midwife and health visitor.

Career profiling

For the individual

The process of career profiling allows the individual more autonomy for the individual to reflect on their experience. It enables the individual to develop a pathway through their career. Once the profile is completed it can be used as part of the requirements for United Kingdom Central Council Post Registration Education and Practice requirements (UKCC, 1990). It will also assist the individual in identifying future academic, managerial and clinical experience in order to deliver a higher quality of healthcare service to the purchaser/client.

The main purpose of this profile is to reflect on past achievements in order to identify an action plan for future developments. The individual requires the assistance of an individual adviser who has the knowledge relating to internal learning opportunities. They should also have a clear understanding of potential AP(E)L (accreditation of prior experiential learning) issues to draw on their wider knowledge and expertise relating to the wider implications of career development within a given organisation.

Completing the profile is a valuable exercise in itself for the individual. It provides a systematic approach to reflect on the individual career to date. It offers the opportunity to take time to assess their career and identify further areas of study and/or experience they may require in order to enhance the practice.

The career profile aims to be a specific review of the individual's achievements, experience and academic status. The completion of it forms the basis of an action plan that can be used by the individual to guide them through future experiential and academic pathways to enhance practice.

This process can also be used to fulfil PREP requirements, be used for a job interview, or within an individual performance review (IPR) process. The profile can also be used as evidence to negotiate for further study and experience, with their relevant line manager, that will enhance the overall quality care of the organisation.

For the organisation

Career profiling is a tool that reflects the individual needs of the practitioner but also assists the organisation in their planning. While reviewing an individual's experience and training, wider perspectives of the organisational and individual work areas can be obtained (Ward, 1997). Career profiling can help the organisation with the basis for a training needs analysis, save money on courses that the individual may attend that are not relevant to them as individuals or the organisation for which they work.

The interview process

On completion of this profile it is useful to have an informal interview with an appropriate manager together if possible with an educationalist working within higher education or as stated earlier an individual adviser who can address both perspectives. Hyde and Wright (1997) noted the importance of seeking assistance of significant others from both within and outside the organisation. As they become more familiar with the organisation plan and educational requirements either one can be involved with the individual practitioner. The manager taking on this role should posses a working knowledge of the opportunities within the organisation and their overall plan. They will need to be aware of the organisational policy in relation to moving clinical areas, shadowing of significant others and the availability of options for secondment or financial support. The individual from the institute of higher education should have a general awareness of the opportunities within the area or specialist fields around the country. They should also be familiar with the accreditation of prior (experiential) learning (AP[E]L) system (discussed later in this chapter). The educationalist and/or manager is often able to draw from the nurse, midwife or health visitor those areas of expertise that they hold in a specific area of care, or identify relevant academic qualifications and relevant experience gained through their practice. Three people spending time to reflect and concentrate on the practitioner's profile provides a rich source of experience and knowledge for action planning.

As this is not a formal accreditation of prior learning process, for those who wish to pursue a course of study, they may also be required to submit the profile to an institution of higher education to gain recognition for accreditation of prior learning towards a course of study or as access onto higher academic levels of study.

The AP(E)L process

Courses offered to nurses, midwives and health visitors are mainly provided within the colleges of higher education. The move in higher education has been to accredit courses with credit accumulation points (CATS) that can be traded in when moving from different institutions towards higher level courses or to obtain credit as part of a course. Many institutions offer an accreditation of prior learning (APL) or accreditation of prior experiential learning (AP[E]L) procedure. The individual must access this procedure for the college/university in which they intend to continue to study. CATS points can only be given in relation to a course and are not awarded as an award in themselves. Individuals can also gain recognition for learning from their experience (experiential learning). This involves the individual seeking credit to produce, usually in the form of a profile, a selection of the learning that has taken place through practice. It should contain relevant theories that have been put into place. For example a ward manager who has implemented a new method of nursing and has implemented and carried through the management of change process. Learning on a formal course comes from the theory and then putting it into practice. This latter form of learning comes from learning the theory or generating theory as the change is taking place. Accreditation of learning is not as easy for the individual as they will have to demonstrate learning at the academic level of the course for which they are seeking accreditation.

The CATS points that are awarded for this process are given at a level of study (see *Table 7.1*).

Table 7.1: Summary of CATS points

Level	**Equivalent study**	**Examples of access to:**	
		Courses	Next level
1	Certificate	RGN, RMN, RMNH etc.	120 points
2	Diploma	P2K, Dip HE, DPSN	120 points
3	Degree (Hons)	BSc, BA, Current ENB courses	120 points
4	Masters Degree (post graduate)	PG Dip, MSc, MA	120–150 points

They may be specific or general points towards a course. Specific points may mean that this course contains a research methods unit at 12 level 2 credits, the individual has undergone the same module, either at this or a similar institution and has been awarded the points. These 12 points are then accredited for the individual and they do not resubmit the same work they have completed. These specific points must however have currency ie. completed usually within the last five years. Some professional courses, for example specialist practitioner award reduces to two year period. General credits are points that are not awarded for specific modules/units ie. the individual has completed some teaching and it has been deemed to be equal to a given amount of points. The individual may exchange these points as part of the course as an optional module/unit but not identified as a specific module. Each institution will identify the amount that the individual is allowed in total to accredit from any named course.

Completing the documentation

The proforma used for career profiling is adapted from the CPD Package (IPD, 1995) for the healthcare provider. It is a tool for the individual practitioner and can be completed by them alone or ideally with the manager and educationalist. For the complete proforma see *Appendix XI*. It is useful if this process can be completed in line with the individual performance review (see *Chapter 3* and *4*) and a copy should be included as this reflects the agreed objectives with their direct line manger.

The document is divided into eight sections these include:

- occupational status
- previous experience
- external activities/positions
- previous learning
- personal expertise
- career objectives
- development plan
- overall summary.

The following text will address each of these sections and suggest material that can be included.

Occupational status

This involves reviewing the current position the individual holds. The section includes:

- name
- current position
- department unit
- commencement date
- line manager
- current responsibilities
- current projects (ie. within the last year)
- other employment.

The section notes the date and time the individual has been in post. It also notes the level of experience they have obtained through the post they hold. Current responsibilities include a brief outline of the role the individual takes on. This is not always the same as a job description, and should include how the individual perceives their current role.

Current projects may include those that are completed on approved courses (ie. English National Board or accredited through a centre of higher education), within practice for instance as part of a bigger research project, or identified as an area within the individual performance review. Or for personal reasons because they want to test out a theory of their own or research they have read. It should also include informal projects that the individual may have performed as part of their role, for example the introduction of policies/procedures, writing of standards, introducing new documentation or methods of working, introducing research into practice, link nurse roles, member of specialist groups, rostering, etc. Individuals often fail to identify the additional roles they perform in their day to day duties.

Other work includes formal or voluntary work, paid or unpaid. These other experiences may also affect the performance of the individual and identify different skills that they posses.

Previous experience

It is useful to complete this section in reverse chronological order as the experience may become dated after a period of time. This section will include the following:

- job position
- job title
- date from—to
- authority/trust
- experience gained.

As each job is recorded the individual should take particular care when completing the experience gained. This should not just include the type of work eg. staff nurse on a gynaecological ward, but the actual experience obtained while in that position which may have been different from all the other staff nurses who have also worked as staff nurses in the gynaecological wards.

The individual may also wish to identify if the job has changed around them eg. as wards change their focus of care, or internal rotation, as these provide new experiences. The nurse working within a hospital that specialises in gynaecology may state that she has only had one job as she has never had an interview since she commenced there. On further questioning the nurse has worked at some stage on every unit in the hospital from out patients, post surgical to theatres and has had a wealth of experiences to draw on.

External activities/positions

Many nurses, midwives and health visitors can become very focused on their role as a practitioner, and do not always recognise the other skills they posses. This section includes:

- type of activity
- date from—to
- experience.

The experience may include the guide leader who may not be able to demonstrate management or leadership responsibilities in their clinical area, but may be performing these tasks with the group they run on a regular basis. Or the individual who is providing a voluntary service to a group of individuals in the community eg. elderly or nursery care, may possess skills that they are not using in their main area of employment. These skills then need to be recognised and developed within practice.

Previous learning

Again this section should include professional and personal achievements. It is useful to identify dates as this often can relate to the credit accumulation system within an institution of higher education. This section includes:

- qualification/award
- awarding body/institution
- date obtained
- comments relating to the contents and learning.

Often individuals note the title of the course of qualification of the award but fail to note the content of the programme. With the accumulation and accreditation of programmes an individual should not be required to repeat learning from one course to another and can often accredit previous learning within other courses when commencing further studies. It is useful to note the credit ratings if known of the programme for future record and to summarise these are identified in *Table 7.2.* The credit rating between individual institutes of higher education is not always clear when transferring these points. The individual should therefore check the currency and value with the institute they wish to continue their studies at.

Table 7.2: Summaries of credit ratings

Qualification/ Courses	Institution	Year/Duration	Cert/Credit level
Summary of CATS points:		Academic level:	

To give some idea of the worth of the credit points it must first be noted their current value. Some courses over time may devalue in points unless the individual can identify that they have developed their knowledge since the completion.

Expertise

This section relates to the capabilities of the individual. For the purpose of exercise the section is broken down into three sections:

- specialist/clinical
- managerial
- personal.

These should include all the skills that the individual possess not just those performed on the job. It provides a summary that will help the individual note where their strengths and weaknesses lie. Experience indicates that this is the section that the individual finds the most difficult to focus on.

Summary of current position

This summary should highlight the experience and learning that the individual has obtained within the job.

Career objectives

It is useful here to take a wider view of the individual's career and to start with a five year plan. Where do you want to be in five years — still in nursing? Do you want to be in the same speciality? At a higher grade? Do you want to move in a different direction? It is these questions that will form the basis of the action plan. If the answer is not in nursing then goals can be set to achieve the outcome as for any other question. If all the answers are to remain the same for personal reasons, then the plan to identify continual updating and delivery of care is still vital for that individual.

Once the long term goal is defined these can be broken down into shorter goals for instance the next 12 months, in order to start the process for the longer term.

It may be that the individual has identified several options in this section. It should not necessarily be reduced to one, but with the manager and educationalist a plan can be drawn up for all identified and the individual may be able to pursue two or more lines at once, or identify which is the most appropriate route for them. It is always the individual's ultimate decision as motivation for development must come from them.

Development plan

This section will include several headings:

On the job learning

- project work

  title

  details

  objectives

  level of need — essential/highly desirable/ desirable/ develops career

- work exposure

  title

  details

  objectives

  level of need – essential/highly desirable/desirable/develops career

Off the job

- secondments/shadowing

  title

  details

  objectives

  level of need — essential/highly desirable/desirable/ develops career

Other learning

- directed reading/individual coaching/other

  title

  details

  objectives

  level of need — essential/highly desirable/desirable/develops career.

It is useful here to identify the desirability in the light of the development plan. To identify the degree at which these experiences are of value to the individual and the organisation in which they work.

The overall summary: personal development plan

This is the final stage of the of the career profile. It is useful if this can be completed by the manager and educationalist as it provides the opportunity to check that what they have discussed is appropriate for the individual and the organisation for which they work. The action plan at this stage could still include more than one option. The aim of the process is not necessarily to tie the individual down to a pathway but to identify possibilities for the practitioner, identifying the professional, governmental and organisational requirements.

A copy, with the individual's permission, of the plan should then be sent to the individual's manager to enable further development within the IPR process, thereby linking the organisation's and individual's goals.

Conclusion

This process is aimed a the individual practitioner. It is their future learning and development that should be paramount. The manager and educationalist will provide relevant information in order to identify the individual's goals, within the constraints of the organisation and profession, and will help the individual identify their strengths and weaknesses in gaining the required skills and knowledge. The constraints, drivers and forces of career development are included in this process (as described in *Chapters 2* and *5*).

References

Hyde J, Wright A (1997) self development. *Nurs Management* **4**(3): 10–11

Institute of Personnel and Development (1995) CPD package launch. *People Management* 5th October

United Kingdom Central Council (1990) *Post Registration Education and Practice.* UKCC, London

Ward C (1997) *An Exploration of Macro vs. Micro Approaches to Identifying the Training and Development Needs of Qualified Nursing Staff.* Unpublished MBA Thesis.University of Warwick

Appendix I

An example of an acute trust's external and internal issues relating to training and development

External	Internal
Political/Legal White papers Policies-executive letters etc. Health and safety Risk management Litigation EEC regulations Working time directives Flexible employment National Occupational standards/NVQ Links with educational consortia	**Business Plan** Human resource management strategy Information system strategy: - training and development issues - process of care Quality strategy Marketing strategy Commitment to Investors in People
Sociological Changes in family structure Women and work Geographical mobility General education Public expectations Continuous learning Workforce expectations Health of the Nation/Health Promotions Social divisions Attitudes to learning/accreditation	**System/Standards** Policies/procedures/protocols Quality strategy -clinical audit Training plan Nursing competencies Communication systems IPR Clinical effectiveness Career pathways Organisational audit

Demographics	Attitudes/Values and Beliefs
Age of population Changing healthcare needs Age of workforce Women in workforce Mature students local population Retirement age Skills shortages	Psychomotor versus cognitive skills Facilitation of learning opportunities Experiential and academic opportunities Internal Vs external provision Organisational and individual responsibility Forms of assessment of knowledge/skills - accreditation Vs non-accreditation Resource commitment Balance of theory and practice Staff involvement Resourcing
Economics	**Politics**
VFM - best practice Public accountability Competition Effectiveness Skills mix	Directorate structure Centralisation Vs decentralisation Communication structures Qualified Vs unqualified debate
Technology	
Changing healthcare provision Information technology - learning need/opportunity NHS Internet	

Appendix II

An example of an acute trust's SWOT analysis

Strengths	Weaknesses
Training strategy	Links-business plan with training and development
Committed staff	No standard appraisal/IPR approach
IPR good in some areas	No true training strategy
Competencies in place in some areas	No systematic identification of need
Links with consortium	Role clarification - some areas
Retention - senior nurses	Priorities not defined
Training and development group	Lack of frameworks/ standards/ continuity
Internal skills/knowledge	Knowledge of training/ education and learning opportunities
In house courses	Time resources
Medical librarian/resources	Reactive not proactive
Preceptorship - nursing	Limited sharing - skills/knowledge
On-site School of Nursing	Size/management - training budget
Rotational programme - nurses	Weak performance management - lack of true accountability
Multidisciplinary working	

Opportunities	Threats
Address weaknesses	New White Paper
New White Paper	Litigation/risk management
Investors in People	Competition- local trusts
Education Consortium	Recruitment and retention
Improve performance management	Loss of accreditation
Estabilish-systems/standards	Poor morale
Training and development strategy	Apathy
Strategic alliances	Failure to meet strategic objectives
Management development	Internal politics
Continuous professional development	Standard maintenance
MCI management standards	Loose recognition - training posts
TEC money	Skills mix issues
Proactive not reactive	Reactive not proactive

Appendix III

An example of objectives/action plans from a training and development strategy

(NB as these are only examples no individuals have been named as responsible, ordinarily however this would be essential)

1. To ensure that the strategy is proactive and dynamic. The training and development group will be the Trusts representative group — overseeing its development and implementation

Action Plan: *Representative membership clearly defined by the end of April. Terms of reference defined by May*

2. To establish effective communication systems

Action Plan: *Review communication strategy by the end of June. Evaluate team briefing by the end of August*

3. To establish effective performance management

Action plans: *Sub-groups will define competencies for the following groups by the end of September:*

1. Nursing

2. Paramedics

3. Managers/Secretarial/Adminisatration staff

4. Support workers

5. Doctors

A new performance management system linked to MBO (management by objectives) for managers, and competencies for other groups of staff will be identified by the end of October.

Training will take place for managers in November

A common IPR system based on competencies and/or objectives will be launched in December and introduced for all grades of staff

4. Definition of training and development needs will be based on systematic data collection methods

Action Plan: *A training needs anaylisis to be undertaken for all managers by the end of September. Futher appropriate TNA's will be identified on an annual basis. Individual departments and directorates will develop individual action plans based on data collected via IPR process*

5. Organisational and personal development needs will be linked.

Action Plan: *All staff to have had IPR by next April. A systematic approach to Continuous Professional Development (CPD) will be identified for nursing and paramedics by the end of September. Support systems for personal development profiling (PDP) will be introduced for the above groups by the end of October.*

Appendix IV

Examples of potential sources of funding (RCN,1998)

Organisations which offer scholarships and grants

RCN Trevor Clay Scholarship. Department of Nursing Policy and Practice. Awards, Royal College of Nursing, 20 Cavendish Square, London, W1M 0AB.

Hospital Saving Association. c/o Moira Lambert, RCN Department of Nursing, Practice and Policy. Address as above.

Peter Holgate Scholarship for occupational health students of the RCN institute. Contact details as above.

Florence Nightingale Foundation. 1 Grosvenor Cresecent, London, SW1 7EH.

Smith and Nephew Foundation Bursaries. Secretary to the Trustees, Smith and Nephew Foundation, 2 Temple Place, Victoria Embankment, London, WC2R 3BP.

The Nightingale Fund Council. 108, Brancaster Lane, Purley, Surrey, CR8 1HH.

Educational Grants Advisory Service. The Family Welfare Association puts students in touch with sources of help from educational trusts and other organisations. Helpful for single parents or those with a disability. c/o The Family Welfare Association, 501–505 Kingsland Road, London, E8 4A1.

Career Development Loans (CDLs). Operated on behalf of the Employment Department by Barclays Co-operative and Clydesdale banks. Apply to a local branch for details.

References

The Directory of Grant Making Trusts published by Charities Aid Foundation. Available from main reference libraries.

Educational Grants Directory 1998/9 published by the Directory of Social Change, 24 Stephenson Way, London, NW1 2DP.

Student Grants and Loans: A Brief Guide issued by the Department for Education and Employment, Student Support Division, Mowden Hall, Staindrop Road, Darlington, DL3 9BG. Tel. 01325 392822.

Appendix V

Example of G grade Competencies in an acute hospital

Competencies of a G Grade ward/departmental manager

1. Clinical/professional role

1.1 Patient care programmes

- able to assess, plan, implement and evaluate individual programmes of care, taking into account specific needs
- able to record care using a problem-solving approach
- able to maintain standards of record keeping within the area
- able to manage a case load of clients
- able to co-ordinate care programmes.

1.2 Professional leadership

- demonstrate knowledge of key professional developments and the implications for practice in their area
- demonstrate knowledge and understanding of key professional issues
- able to transfer this knowledge/understanding to other staff
- able to ensure that professional standards are maintained
- demonstrate effectiveness as a role model.

1.3 Teaching/Coaching

- able to assess and teach others in a clinical setting.

1.4 Patient/client advocacy

- able to act on client's behalf and clearly represent their views to others.

1.5 Practice/research

- demonstrate clinical competence
- demonstrate competence (knowledge/skills) relating to expansion of role, as defined by organisational standards/protocols
- be aware of current research/approaches to patient care and demonstrate this in practice
- demonstrate an understanding of the principles of research and clinical effectiveness
- able to take an active role in the process of research and clinical effectiveness.

2. Leadership and change role

2.1 Team-building

- able to select, develop and motivate a team
- able to lead a team towards achieving common objectives
- able to work effectively within various teams eg. the nursing team, the multidisciplinary team and the directorate team
- able to advise/assist and counsel other members of the nursing team.

2.2 Vision/leadership

- able to demonstrate a clear idea of direction, and belief in the job
- able to turn the vision into a workable agenda.

2.3 Communication skills

- able to communicate effectively both verbally and in writing, with other members of the organisation, and with patients and their relatives.

2.4 Delegation

- able to match responsibilities to the capabilities and workload of team members.

2.5 Conflict resolution

- able to recognise, prevent and diffuse potential areas of conflict
- demonstrate a proactive approach to complaints management.

2.6 Assertiveness/negotiating skills

- able to prepare and present arguments based on facts, convince others and resolve claims for competing resources.

2.7 Standard maintenance

- able to set, monitor and maintain standards of care
- able to take appropriate action if standards are not being met.

2.8 Creator/innovator

- able to continuously innovate and enable other staff to do so
- able to identify areas for practice development.

2.9 Networking

- able to establish and maintain a network of contacts beyond the ward/ departmental area.

3. Organisational skills

3.1 Budgeting

- demonstrate an understanding of the ward/ departmental budget
- able to actively participate in establishment setting
- demonstrate budgetary awareness in the planning and implementation of care.

3.2 Objective setting

- demonstrate clear understanding of organisational goals
- able to set ward/departmental objectives which reflect organisational targets
- able to achieve objectives.

3.3 Problem solving /decision making

- demonstrate a systematic, yet flexible and innovative approach to problem solving
- able to make decisions and act accordingly.

3.4 Managing the environment

- able to maintain an environment conducive to patient/staff welfare and health education.

3.5 Individual performance management

- able to assess the performance of others, both as a continuous process, and as part of the formal performance review programme
- able to monitor sickness and absence, and take action where required
- able to recognise the development needs of others and take appropriate action
- able to identify learning opportunities and advise others accordingly.

3.6 Skill mix management

- demonstrates an understanding of skill mix implications when managing annual leave, study leave and rostering.

3.7 Interviewing /selection

- able to participate in the recruitment and selection process
- demonstrates an understanding of equal opportunity policies, and organisational recruitment policy.

4. Personal skills

4.1 Self management

- able to prioritise and act accordingly
- demonstrates awareness of personal strengths and weaknesses
- recognises personal and workload limitations and can take appropriate action
- able to self start and self motivate.

4.2 Interpersonal skills

- able to interact with clients/visitors and colleagues in a professional and approachable manner.

4.3 Professional conduct

- aware of and able to maintain professional standards of conduct as per the UKCC code
- able to take action if others do not meet required standards.

4.4 Organisational conduct

- aware of and able to maintain standards of organisational conduct. For example:
  - uniform policy
  - sickness and absence policy
  - reliability and punctuality.
- health and safety policies
- infection control policy
- other hospital policies
- able to take action if others do not meet required standards.

Appendix VI

Questionnaire design

Question types

Consideration must be given as to what you are trying to find out. Obviously the more structured the question the easier it is to analyse the results. At the same time this may not yield the more qualitative data required. Youngman (1986) lists 7 types of questions that may be used. They include:

1. Open

Open questions are utilised in order to give respondents the opportunity to state their own views and/or preferences. An example in TNA being:

> *What do you feel are your own personal development needs*

Although potentially yielding very useful information and less restricting than some of the following approaches, this type of question can be very difficult to analyse.

2. List

In this case a list of items is offered, any of which can be chosen. An example in TNA may be:

> *Please indicate your current area of work:*
>
> - *acute (secondary) care*
> - *primary care*
> - *private sector*
> - *charity organisations*
> - *unemployed.*

Potential difficulties in this type of question are that, unless broad categories are used, and unless the list is explicitly defined, then categories may be missed or questions may be ambiguous. In most cases it is useful to include a category stating '*other*' and asking respondents to indicate what this is.

3. Category

In this case a list is again provided but the respondent can only fit into one category. An example of this includes:

How old are you?

15-24

25-34 etc.

(NB in this example remember that questions should only be asked if they are absolutely relevant to the study. That is questions relating to age, gender, race etc. should only be asked if there is a purpose).

4. Ranking

Respondents can be asked to place something in rank order. For example:

In the following list of 20 management competencies please rank them in order of your perceived development need. For example if you perceive 'Financial management' to be your greatest need this would score 1. Whereas if you felt 'Self management' is least needed, then this would rank 20.

Strategies development ❐

Objective setting ❐

Evaluating and improving performance ❐

Managing activities ❐

Managing change ❐

Financial management ❐

Self management ❐

Creating effective team-working ❐

Maintaining effective team-working ❐

Recruitment/selection of personnel ❐

Team and individual development ❐

Lead team to achieve objectives ❐

Delegate work to others ❐

Deal with poor performance in team ❐

Ongoing maintenance of individual performance ❐

Communication with others — verbally ❐

Communication with others — in writing ❐

Establish quality assurance/audit systems ❐

Establish/maintain quality strategy ❐

Project management skills ❐

(For examples of how to use self assessment ranking questionnaires in TNA see Flynn and Diaz, 1988)

5. Scale

There are various types of scales which can be used, examples include:

Graphic rating

Here the respondents are asked to give their opinion of something against two ends of a continuum:

How would you rate your Information Technology training provided by the Personnel Department? (Place a tick in the appropriate space on the scale)

Excellent	1	2	3	4	5	6	7	Poor

Likert scales

Often used to measure attitudes, this approach is used to establish respondents' views on a topic, asking them to indicate along a continuum scale whether they strongly agree or disagree with statements. An example of one statement is:

Motivated people can meet their own development needs within this organisation

Strongly agree	Agree	Neither Agree/Nor Disagree	Disagree	Strongly disagree

6. Quantity

Fairly straightforward, here the respondent is asked to give a number relating to the question. For example:

How many individuals are you responsible for managing?

7. Grid

A table or grid is provided to record answers to two or more questions at the same time.

Question wording

There are a number of key issues to avoid when wording questions, examples being:

Ambiguity

There is a danger that what the researcher means when asking the question is perceived differently by respondents due to ambiguity. For example avoid the use of categories such as 'average'. This can mean many things to different people. An example of an ambiguous question is given below.

How much time do you spend studying each week?

- *too much*

- *a lot*
- *average*
- *a little*
- *not enough.*

What information would this give you apart from the individual's perception of what is too much or average? What is meant by the word studying? It is more likely in this instance that more precise answers are required relating to exactly how much time is spent in particular types of study.

Leading questions

Beware of leading questions that are a result of your individual bias. For example:

> *Do you agree that you should have a say in what your learning needs are?*

It would be difficult to answer no to this question.

Double questions

Although obvious it is amazing the number of researchers who make this mistake. An example being:

> *Do you have access to external and internal courses?*

Here the respondent may feel that they have access to one or the other, however would they state no if they believed it was only one? How useful would this information then be?

Offensive questions

Obviously one must be careful not to ask questions which are likely to cause offence. It is more likely however, that researchers will ask questions which are considered sensitive areas. Examples may relate to age, gender or race. As stated earlier it is essential to consider whether questions are really necessary for the purpose of the study. If so, it may be useful to give potential respondents the reasons (providing that this does not potentially affect the response), or ensure anonymity.

Questionnaire layout

Having carefully thought out and structured the question types, it is essential that this is not spoiled by an untidy approach. The following should therefore be considered:

- questionnaires should always be typed
- instructions should be clear
- keep the questionnaire as short as possible, whilst still ensuring that the questions adequately cover the objectives of your study
- leave enough space between questions for answers
- leave sensitive questions until later, start with straightforward answers eg. biographical details
- ask for other opinions before distribution
- arrange a pilot study to test not only the results within the responses but also asking for opinions regarding the questionnaire itself.

Piloting and distribution

As stated above it is essential to pilot a questionnaire both in terms of evaluating the instrument itself, and also to start initial analysis in order to identify any potential ambiguity, and to assess whether the analysis can be undertaken in practice. The following issues need to be considered in relation to distribution:

- how will you practically distribute it. Personally or by mail? If by mail it is useful to either contact respondents beforehand or ensure that a covering letter is provided which outlines the purpose of the study. Otherwise, in the days of questionnaire-overload there is a danger that yours may be the one immediately dispatched to the waste paper bin
- what are you stating about confidentiality/ anonymity?
- have you set a return date and to whom?

- do you need to enclose a self-addressed, stamped envelope?
- do you intend to remind non-respondents?

Analysis

Although analysis has been left until the end of this section, this is not the stage it should represent in your study. Decisions on the analysis approach should be made alongside questionnaire design.

When deciding which types of questions are to be used it is imperative to ensure that you have the expertise and resources to analyse appropriately.

References

Bell J (1993) *Doing Your Research project.* Open University Press, Milton Keynes

Borg WR (1981) *Applying Educational Research. A Practical Guide for Teachers.* Longman, New York

Flynn JP, Diaz AA (1988) Identifying management training needs for social service workers in Madrid, Spain. *International Social Work* **31**(88): 145–56

Youngman MR (1986) *Analysing Questionnaires.* University of Nottingham School of Education, Nottingham

Appendix VII

Style of interview and types of questions

Style of interview can be considered on a continuum of formal and informal, dependant on the approach adopted. The overall approach may be structured/semi-structured or unstructured. In relation to TNA, the latter is not recommended, particularly as we have adopted a systems based approach based on measurement against defined standards.

The structured approach may be totally mechanistic utilising a questionnaire that is completed by the interviewer from responses that the interviewee gives. Alternatively there may be more flexibility utilising a semi-structured approach, responding to the interviewee. The latter may enable greater depth in data collection as the interviewee may relax more in a less formal approach. The disadvantage of course is that this may then be more difficult to record and to subsequently analyse.

Whatever approach is used the guidelines given earlier relating to the design of questions used in questionnaires also applies to interview schedules.

Bias minimisation

As stated above there is more risk of bias in the interview situation, partly because as Sellitz *et al* (1962) points out '*interviewers are human beings and not machines*'. In addition there is an additional potential response effect between interviewers and interviewees, which can result in the interviewee wanting to please and the interviewer trying to seek out answers that meet their preconceived beliefs (Borg, 1981). Although it is difficult to totally eliminate potential bias, Bell (1993) states that awareness of the issue can help to minimise it.

In TNA therefore the interviewer must consider their own values and beliefs and how these may influence the interview. Attempts must then be made to be as objective as possible.

Data collection

Consideration must be given as to how data will be collected:

- will a questionnaire be completed by the interviewer from responses given?
- will interview notes be made? If so is there a need for a prompt list?
- will the session be tape-recorded for future analysis?
- how will data be verified with the interviewee? At the time or later?

Data analysis

As with questionnaires, this should be considered when designing the interview schedule. Often however, particularly if using a number of open questions, it is difficult to begin analysis, until a number of interviews have been undertaken. A useful approach to analysing qualitative data from interview situations is that advocated by Ritchie and Spencer (1994). They suggest that by a process of abstraction and conceptualisation, recurrent themes and issues can be identified, these can then be categorised into:

- priority issues — those informed by the initial aims
- emergent issues — those raised by respondents
- analytical themes — recurrence or patterning of particular views or experience.

From this, overall themes can then be identified and full interpretation take place.

References

Bell J (1993) *Doing Your Research project.* Open University Press, Milton Keynes

Borg WR (1981) *Applying Educational Research. A Practical Guide for Teachers.* Longman, New York

Rictchie J, Spencer L (1994) Qualifying data analysis for applied policy research. In: Bryman A, Burgess RG *Analysing Qualitative Data.* Routledge, London

Sellitz C, Jahoda M, Deutsch M, Cook S (1962) *Research Methods in Social Relations* 2nd ed. Rinehart and Winston, New York

Appendix VIII

An example of a manager's preparation form for IPR

Manager's preparation form Part 1: Past and Present Performance	
Name:	**Area:**
1.	Using previously identified objectives and/or competencies, note the key areas for discussion eg. Strengths, weaknesses
2.	Over the past 12 months what have been the individual's key achievements? Have there been any obstacles to them carrying out their work?
3.	Are you utilising the individual's skills and abilities?

Part 2: Future performance	
4.	List any potential future objectives you would like to agree. How might these be measured?
5.	What do you perceive the individual's development needs to be? How might these be met?
6.	What opportunities are there for individual role development? Does the individual have potential for promotion? How might this be achieved?

Appendix IX

An example of an individual staff member's preparation form for IPR

Name:	Area:
1.	Are previously identified objectives and/or competencies still appropriate? If not, note how these should be changed.
2.	In relation to the competencies or your defined role, what do you feel you are good at?
3.	Are there any aspects of your role that you are doing less well in?
4.	What do you believe to be your major achievements in the last 12 months? Have there been any obstacles?

5.	Do you believe your skills and abilities are being utilised? If not what needs to be done?
6.	What future objectives would you like to agree?
7.	What do you feel your development needs are? How might these be met?
8.	Where would you like to go from here? What direction would you like your future career to take?

Appendix X

Performance review: individual interview record form

Section 1	
1.	Have previously agreed performance standards eg. objectives and/or competencies been met? (Comment on level of achievement and whether any obstacles existed)
2.	Were identified development needs met?
Section 2	
3.	What are the agreed objectives for the next review period? How and when will these be measured?
4.	What are the agreed future development needs?
Section 3	
Overall comments of reviewing manager	
Signature Date Comments of individual	
Signature Date Comments of reviewing manager's manager	
Signature Date	

Appendix XI

Personal career profile proforma

Occupational Status
Name:
Current position:
Department/unit:
Commencement date:
Line manager:
Current responsibilities:
Current projects (within the last 12 months):
Other employment:

Previous Experience

1. **Job position:**
   Job title:
   Date from-to:
   Employing authority trust:
   Experience gained:

2. **Job position:**
   Job title:
   Date from-to:
   Employing authority trust:
   Experience gained:

3. **Job position:**
   Job title:
   Date from-to:
   Employing authority trust:
   Experience gained:

4. **Job position:**
   Job title:
   Date from-to:
   Employing authority trust:
   Experience gained:

5. **Job position:**
   Job title:
   Date from-to:
   Employing authority trust:
   Experience gained:

External Activities/Positions

1. **Type of activity:**

   Date from-to:

   Experience gained:

2. **Type of activity:**

   Date from-to:

   Experience gained:

3. **Type of activity:**

   Date from-to:

   Experience gained:

Previous Learning

1. **Qualification/Award**

   Awarding body/insitutuion

   Date obtained

   Comments relating to contents of course and learning:

2. **Qualification/Award**

   Awarding body/insitutuion

   Date obtained

   Comments relating to contents of course and learning:

3. **Qualification/Award**

   Awarding body/insitutuion

   Date obtained

   Comments relating to contents of course and learning:

4. **Qualification/Award**

   Awarding body/insitutuion

   Date obtained

   Comments relating to contents of course and learning:

Summary of academic status
(See *Table 7.2*)

Personal Expertise

Specialist/clinical skills/knowledge

Managerial skills/knowledge

Personal skills/knowledge

Summary of current position:

Career Objectives

5 year plan:

3 year plan:

Next 12 months:

Career Development Plan

Name:

Date:

Action plan option 1:

Action plan option 2:

Action plan option 3:

Signed. . . . . **Date.** . . . .

Index